WOMEN AND THE SUN

by the same author

BEASTS AND MEN
THE SEED
THE CORAL BARRIER
THE FUGITIVE

WOMEN
AND
THE SUN

Pierre Gascar

Stories translated by

MERLOYD LAWRENCE

LILY EMMET

VENABLE HERNDON

URSULE MOLINARO

JEAN STEWART

An Atlantic Monthly Press Book

Little, Brown and Company

BOSTON   TORONTO

FIRST ENGLISH LANGUAGE EDITION

The author wishes to thank the following for permission to reprint material which first appeared in their pages: *Mademoiselle*, *Harper's Bazaar*, *San Francisco Review*.
'The Asylum' is reprinted by permission of the publisher from *New French Writing* edited by Georges Borchardt. (New York, 1961) Copyright 1961 by Criterion Books, Inc.

ATLANTIC-LITTLE, BROWN BOOKS
ARE PUBLISHED BY
LITTLE, BROWN AND COMPANY
IN ASSOCIATION WITH
THE ATLANTIC MONTHLY PRESS

*Published simultaneously in Canada
by Little, Brown & Company (Canada) Limited*

PRINTED IN GREAT BRITAIN

Contents

The story MARBLE
is dedicated
to Alice

The Cistern

THE SUMMER seemed longer, fiercer, than all those which had gone before. Every year it was this way. No one ever remembered how the light blazed down on the whitened earth, the searing heat. No doubt this was deliberate; a lapse of memory to give life a little more shade.

The village was destitute of shade, more so than any other. There were but a few trees. Besides the church and the cistern, there were only three houses, standing apart from one another. Nearly all the inhabitants lived in *cuevas*, caves hollowed out of the knolls which crowd this slope of the Sierra Nevada.

With nothing projecting, nothing to hold shade, the village lay exposed to the sun all day long. During the most scorching hours, there was no trace of life whatsoever, only a kind of absence which intensified the heat. A mysterious absence, a strange period that was in part the age of light, in part the age of man. Underground, children were being raised; beneath the desert, people went on talking, making love; and every day, towards noon, the men would return from the fields with impassive faces to take shelter, for a time, in death.

Here and there, to be sure, a doorway, limewashed blue,

opened into the side of one of the clay knolls; here and there a
short chimney, also blue, rose from the pale weeds on the top,
domesticating the landscape, converting its outlines into architectural forms. But once a man crossed over one of these exotic
blue thresholds, he was lost; he disappeared into tunnels which
seemed to go on forever; he entered a different realm; he
groped along walls where bits of mica gleamed, blind creatures
lurked, and roots came to an end. He slept in an upside-down
world, feeling, on either side of him, like vast unfolded wings,
the successive layers laid down by each geological strata, all
this beneath a ceiling of death in which only a grain of quartz
was alive.

Outside: fire. And sometimes wind, a short-lived wind which
came from afar, ruffling the grass on the hills as far as the eye
could see, a wind which had grazed the red towers shaped and
laid bare by erosion, in the mountains just before Elva, and
which would cross the Sierra and die over the sea, against
waves running in the opposite direction.

A village without houses, men without horizons, and a summer without end: all this merged into a kind of eternity. But an
eternity of so many colours! In the evening, the colour of faded
or ill-fired brick; at noon, whiteness, glowing through the clay
dust raised by the wind; and finally, in the morning, the mauve
shadows which would not last, but meanwhile dappled the
distant hills like patches of dwarf vegetation.

These shifting tones – and there were other gradations,
according to the time of day – restored a feeling of fertility to a
land sterilized by drought. The evening wore harvest colours,
and there were moments, except in the total whiteness at noon,
when the earth all around Elva seemed more deeply tinted, as
though it had slaked its thirst. To anyone emerging from the
shadowy *cuevas*, the dazzling light and barren earth of summer
created a world of illusion, of diversity, where the variegated
light of day, playing on the hillsides, suggested now wheat, now
esparto grass, or in the mornings, blankets of sweet marjoram
or gentian. The earth underfoot offered stones of all kinds,

onyx, banded quartz, it revealed veins of clay, chalk, sand and powdery humus, overgrown with stubby dry weeds, spiny plants unfolding in star shapes, black insects.

But only water is always water. It was the one constant, badly needed in this world where everything was multiplying, disintegrating in the heat, or dissolving into mirages of light. It was the one language, needed in the world where silence was everywhere, the silence of summer, the silence of high noon at the bottom of ditches, the silence inside the cistern, with ears of grain left by the wind, and footprints in the dust.

The inhabitants of Elva had to go several kilometres from their *cuevas* to draw cloudy water from a mudhole. With their jars hung over the backs of donkeys, they returned to their buried village, along a rocky path. They left footprints, on the surface of the rocks, and later on, inside the three houses of Elva or on the paved floor of the *cuevas*, like the tracks of masons when they leave a house. And these pale imprints, these traces of silent traffic, seemed like prophecies, gave a kind of solemnity to the least motion. They suggested the sudden frugality of existence. Now everything, every step, every gesture, had to count; drought had turned life into a precarious miracle every last trace of which had to be preserved.

There was still time to turn around in one's tracks, catch a glimpse of oneself, as the burning air closed in, time to measure one's progress, which never led anywhere except further into summer, drought, and thirst.

Everything might have been so simple! The rain would have come, one of those long, slow rains which darkens the entire day and rustles on into the night, while, from the threshold of one of the *cuevas*, open to receive the cool air, ears of corn sway back and forth, luminous as yellow lanterns.

A few weeks earlier, one of the inhabitants of Elva had stabbed a man, during a quarrel the cause of which remained unclear. He had been lowered, with ropes, into the empty tank of the cistern, and left there until morning, when the police came. His laments had continued far into the night, resounding against the walls of the vast cement tank.

There was no direct connection between the unusual length of the summer and the man's sorrow or remorse, nothing to connect the drought and this subterranean voice which rang out until dawn, with dogs barking now and then, and yet, ever since then, the footprints had been there in the bottom of the cistern. Only the rain, the return of water, would erase them. Until then, the man's crime would be like a landmark; the rains had already stopped when it happened.

The drought had begun with blood, with a wound, and had raged on like a fever. For others, it is true, the drought had begun with a scorpion encountered on the path leading to the stone Virgin; for still others, with flocks of birds migrating overhead; and finally, for some, with the hardening of voices and faces, way back around April or perhaps a bit earlier, when the ground was still heavy with rain, and hatred could still seem like a crime . . .

Now it is my turn; I am in the bottom of the cistern. My footprints have covered and obliterated those of the man who was here before me. I did not know him well. I was not sure what his quarrel was about. I have always kept to myself in the village. The shed which I use as an auto repair shop lies on the main highway, three kilometres from Elva. I leave the *cueva* where I live very early in the morning and do not return until the evening. My relations with the other people in the village consist of a few trivial remarks when I happen to meet them along the road. They are a little suspicious of me. In Spain today, mechanics are the only men who think.

Perhaps, too, only a mechanic would be perverse enough to have listened to those laments, rising over the village, that evening. It was the voice of the man in the cistern, wailing like a captive muezzin. He must have been drinking, and, alone against these circular walls, he was prolonging the drunken frenzy which had led him to take out his knife and strike. I could not understand what he was saying, and did not really care. Still, his mad raving delighted me. In Spain, there will never be enough dogs howling in the night, never enough warnings of doom.

I was sitting outside at the foot of the little knoll of my *cueva*. I had my own mountain, the whole interior of a mountain, like the hermits in the old paintings I have seen in the Prado. Sometimes they live in half of a gigantic egg, with the jagged edge of the shell resting on the bare ground. They wear beards like Levites, and sit musing. They seem secure from the horrors they contemplate. In the background, naked men and women, thin but with curiously swollen bellies, are strapped to wheels; others are enclosed in a pink glass bubble which a huge frog holds between its feet. Clothing hangs from frail, leafless trees.

I saw nothing like this in the powdery waste which stretched out between the *cuevas* of Elva, beneath the moon. Only the voice of the man confined in the cistern, as I am today, was a reminder that there was more in the world than this pale light and these shadows. The man's voice aroused the dogs. Even more than the moon, or the heat, it prevented them from sleeping. Was it an appeal, an entreaty, or abuse? The dogs' replies were no easier to fathom, but what mattered to me was that this absurd dialogue should continue: it was kindling Spain.

It could never be kindled enough. As far as my eyes could see – and when I closed them, I could see the whole way, from Motril to Huesca, from Jaen to Cabo de Gata – I looked upon ashes. Beneath the barren mountains, the land whitened by too long a summer, the silence of the people, beneath all this a fire lay smouldering. Someone, someday, would have to cry out an alarm.

Meanwhile, my life, like that of the others, although I lived somewhat apart, was a life of aridity, of drought. One Saturday, I left my wooden shed at noon. The heat was unbearable and there was little work. There were fewer cars than ever along the highway.

I walked back along the sandy road at the edge of which

hung feathery roots, some with minute clods of earth, hard as pottery, clinging to them, not so much a road as a huge crack in the earth, one which might have been blamed on the noon-day sun, had not Moors and black peasants with Visigoth ears passed before me along the same road, on their way to a red castle that blended in the distance with the wind-eroded towers, in the hills of clay and quartz, just before Elva.

Dead stream, dried-up river. The riverbeds here are only for men and beasts, torrents of stumbling and thirst. Sometimes even the streams of men and animals run dry. Then I am left to walk alone, morning and evening, with a spade on my back, in the paths of Arabs with their horsehair fans, or those dead peasants, my brothers, a lone mechanic in the heart of Spain, with my grease-covered clothes almost shiny in the sun, and the black fly that keeps me company, darting ahead and settling here and there, on the stones marked with footprints.

That day, I happened to notice the lace of an espadrille lying on the ground, and leaned over to pick it up. It was just a gesture of loneliness. I was about to throw away the frayed lace when a man, who had been following without my noticing him, caught up with me. He was from Elva, but I hardly knew him. He looked at the lace which I was about to throw away and held out his hand.

'If you have no use for it . . .'

I gave it to him. He wound it up and put it in his pocket, looking at me in an unfriendly way. I am a little richer than the others. They lack everything. We continued on our way in silence. The sun had never burned so fiercely. Its vertical rays did not even cast a shadow beneath the high, crumbling banks of the road, as they did in the morning and the evening. Usually, when I went to work, or on my way home, the shadows were there, deeper, more opaque in the distance. As I looked at them I saw men with rifles pressed to the walls of trenches, or worse, dead men with rifles, I feel no regret for any battle, neither those that have raged for centuries, in all corners of this country, or those in my dreams, as I walked along the empty road, with the enemy advancing far in the distance, the sun behind him, now moving forward with dawn, now with dusk, my everyday enemies whom I knew by their numbers, if not by their faces . . .

The man beside me began to talk about the drought. He was sure that it would never rain again. When night fell, there was never even a cloud in the sky. When morning came, the sky was equally pure, always with a feeling of peace and contentment. The sky seemed to have returned to its original state. Until then it had been marred by storms, by the last disturbances of a diluvian age. Now the world was emerging from childhood, as though from a forest full of noise and shadow. Indeed, these burned fields, stretching out as far as the eye could see, wore the colours of eternity.

The man did not say all these things; I am reading into his words and the silences between them. I did not answer him. He seemed surprised at my reticence. Once again he looked at me in an unfriendly manner.

'What are you thinking about?'

I said the first word that came into my mind, a word which gave me pleasure as I said it, for it had a kind of cool brevity and, at the same time, a strangeness, a transparent ring.

'A sluice.'

The man did not know this word and I saw the anger spreading over his thin face.

'A sluice?'

He finally settled the issue by shrugging his shoulders, as though it were understood that I had always been demented. He stopped talking and we parted, with vague goodbyes, just before the door to the first *cueva*.

Later on, the word 'sluice' would become ammunition for my accusers. Tonight, it keeps darting through my mind: a short, sharp, icy word. With this word I had thrown a dagger between the people of Elva and myself.

Why had this word come into my mind? Probably because the heat made me dream of relief, of some kind of solution.

But then, I could have just talked about rain, the way my companion and the other inhabitants of the village did. There are no sluices here. It is an invention of the north; a channel of dark water, its sides covered in velvet slime, a place where people drown. By evoking something which could not exist here, which, besides, would surpass our wildest dreams and might even add to our thirst, I was yielding either to sadism or to raving madness. At least that is what they probably thought. But I wonder now if this word, which passed so suddenly through my mind, had not been a kind of omen.

That day, bored by inactivity, I decided to enlarge my dwelling. For those of us who inhabit *cuevas*, there is no limit to the amount of living space. All we have to do is dig; new rooms are built with a pickaxe. No one needs to be cramped. Rooms multiply beneath the scorched earth. Every *cueva* is a mysterious mansion. Even after being invited to visit it, one does not know how large it is. If one manages to find out, the mystery closes in again the day after one's visit; a room, or at least an alcove, a corridor, or a hole could have been dug in the meanwhile.

It is not always easy to fathom the motives of those who add, in the depths of their dark house, another even darker, more silent, more sepulchral room. What iniquities will it hide? Perhaps the most secret and furtive of all: solitary blasphemy, incest. The darkness, the close odours of the earth, arouse such desires. There is more to Hell than one thinks. At every step along the way, one grows in the strength and the appetites that justify its existence.

But now I'm dreaming. As we dug, we were also fleeing. We were fleeing the summer that was too long, too cruel, the world that was being consumed by its own clarity. I was fleeing the evidence of daylight: the lace which the man wound up so carefully, the brief anger on a face which had not sweated for a long time. This man and those like him had to suffer more, I realized, had to suffer a little more. And I with them. For Spain had to awaken.

I would have given them everything, all the water in the sky.

With my own hands I would have arranged the stones into a basin beneath the spring, then a channel to direct the clear, spurting water, with pebbles at the bottom, marked with white half moons, stripes, rings, the water rushing, spilling over these stone hieroglyphics, over bent grasses, crumbling red earth, racing headlong, twisting and straightening, sometimes even circling about, or losing part of itself in a slow backwash, then gradually gathering force again, endlessly reunited with itself, flowing on and on, swelling like a bow-wave against the pebbles marked with yellow or white eyes, or shredded into thin pennants by branches, and finally reaching the network of *arroyos* the checkerboard of irrigation ditches, the canals of loose soil where, suddenly at rest, yellowed, sleeping beneath a film of grass blades, wisps of straw, dead insects, it slips into the earth through a thousand invisible corridors and sinks to nourish the fertility of China . . . All this I would have given, but first . . .

The most tedious part of digging a new room in a *cueva* was clearing out the dirt. Some of the villagers used it to fill in other rooms which they no longer needed. They lived between these embankments. Filled in on one side, hollowed out on another, their houses zigzagged back and forth like the track of a worm. Sometimes they even changed the location of the front door. A blue frame, like a painted gallows, was left on the side of the knoll. This deserted village, this unreal village, was enough to drive one completely crazy.

I carried the dirt out of my grotto in two large baskets and dumped it, slightly to one side, at the foot of my private knoll. No one saw me; there was no one outside, only the cracks in doorways. When everything is empty, a human presence can become as slim as a blade of grass, as unobtrusive as a knot in a plank of wood. The work was exhausting. I alternated endlessly between light and shadow, between the fire outside and the coolness within. All this just for a place to keep a few car and bicycle tyres; the heat in my repair shop rotted the rubber. And I was afraid of theft. At least these were the only reasons I would admit to myself. Actually, I was looking for a way out of this dazzling prison, this prison which once was Spain.

I was stirring up the earth. It, too, changed colour from one moment to the next, turning pale as I brought it into the light, darkening again as I piled it on the rest, then drying up completely after a moment.

Soon I discovered that it was drying less and less quickly, even though the sun was still as strong as ever. In the back of my *cueva*, I laid my hand, and then my cheek against the wall where I had been digging. It was cooler than usual. Then I burrowed a hole just wide enough for my arms, reached in, and pulled out a handful of moist earth.

Going over to the lantern, I looked at my hand. I noticed the earth could once again be kneaded; it was turning back into bread. And suddenly a frenzy of joy came over me, which I was soon to regret. I wanted to rush out, to shout to the first passer-by, to show him this handful of dark earth, which held the marks of my fingers, to reveal to the men of Elva that there was water in the knoll where I lived, to join hands with them and dig down to the underground spring . . .

I found myself in the bright sunlight. The space between the knolls was no longer entirely empty. A certain distance away, straight ahead of me, a man was beating a sheep. I blinked in the dazzling sunlight and looked again. People sometimes beat their donkeys, but why a sheep?

He was held on a tether which the man pulled towards him, as he raised the large branch with which he was whipping the animal. It was trying to escape, scampering in all directions and slipping in the dust, its head low, bustling feverishly as though it were caught in the midst of the flock, not so much punished as lost, and blind.

A gust of wind lifted the dust, mingled with chaff from the last threshing. The man and the sheep disappeared behind this whirlwind. It brought a smell of stale harvest to the place where I was standing. The summer was beginning to seem like death. Spain, its land turned to ashes, was smoking everywhere, it was disappearing behind a cloud in which one could still make out, as though in a pyre consumed by flames, the profile of a red mountain and a black branch which a man, already almost invisible, was raising above his head, a man who would never again raise a flail above the yellow grain, a man who had lost all his defences, one by one, who had sunken to the final degree of dispossession, and now, wrapped only in a cloud of dust, was reduced to fighting with a lamb.

I opened my hand; the earth had dried. I let it crumble through my fingers. No miracle had happened. No miracles would ever happen in Spain. I went back inside my *cueva*, locked the door and started digging again.

Towards evening, the water began to flow in tiny threads along the wall. It was no more than a seeping, really, and soon disappeared into a crevice. Only when I lifted my lantern, and moved it about, did the wall glisten, catching a reflection and then losing it again. The water did not really exist until I pressed the edge of my hand against the wall, and let it trickle into my palm.

I was not going to dig any more, even though I was sure that the water level was not far away. I would stop here. We would all stop here. We were satisfied. I, with the suggestion of a spring. They, with hope. They would have felt overwhelmed by this hint of a spring. But, for this country's salvation, there had to be a greater desire.

I gathered enough water to wash myself from head to foot. Then I hung a piece of cloth like a curtain over the wall. I lifted it from time to time; the water gave only a faint glimmer, like a tiny creature in the earth. I said to myself that white plants would soon begin sprouting all around.

After I went to bed, I listened carefully for the sound. It was almost inaudible. Anyone unaware of what was there would never have heard it. It was not the trickling or the gurgle, faint as they might be, of running water. Nor even a murmur. It was more like silent motion, far away; the wall was breathing.

I was no longer sleeping alone. Suddenly, I could understand

the loneliness of all those who were asleep in the neighbouring *cuevas*, with a woman or children next to them in the
darkness. These lives do not fill up the space. They cannot
triumph over summer. The sighs, the muttering of sleep, the
whispering of love were no more, in these deep *cuevas*, than a
murmur in a tomb, slowly subsiding, Here, water gleamed,
water, which would never run dry, cool in the heat, bright in
the darkness, fertile . . .

I went back to it the next morning. It was not flowing any
faster. But the trickles of water had dug narrow, winding
grooves into the earth, carving the wall in rococo patterns.
The water was receding slightly, collecting in crevices where
it sparkled like chips of inlaid mirror.

Outdoors, the sun was shining as usual, and the men, who
had been dressed in their Sunday clothes since dawn, were
already overcome by the heat. A little later, they would be
stamping their dusty feet in church. I never went, but for this
I was half-forgiven; in the eyes of the villagers, to be a
mechanic was a religion in itself.

I decided to walk to the town that lay along the highway, not
more than two kilometres from my repair shop. I spent most
of my holidays there, either at the home of friends playing
cards, or at the café where everyone knew me and respected my
knowledge. I was waiting to rent a room there, which had been
promised me for some time. I despised the people of Elva.
Those of the town were no better but there was shade in their
streets, now and then someone was heard singing, and I could
get slowly drunk there on wine, listening to the flies hum in the
sweltering café. It was a kind of sleep.

Often I would withdraw from the conversation and sit with
my eyes wide open, staring at the advertisements and bullfight
posters hung on the walls, behind the unfurling cigarette
smoke. Sometimes Isabela, the waitress, would come over and
touch my shoulder. I would start, and look up. She would smile
at me. She had been my mistress for about a year. However,
we rarely met outside the café. I was waiting for the room.

Isabela was waiting for marriage. I was in no hurry. She chided me for not believing in anything.

That Sunday, towards evening, the man I had met along the road the day before, came into the café. I looked at his espadrilles, to see if he had used the lace. He caught me looking at them and seemed annoyed.

'Hello there, Mister "Sluice" . . .'

He snickered. He had stepped up to the counter, to order a drink. The men who were there asked him why he had called me that. He told them. One of the men thought he knew what the word meant and explained, or at least tried to explain, it to his friends. It was water, water that flowed from one level to another, like a waterfall, but in a more controlled – how could you describe it – a smoother way, in other words mechanized water . . .

'I've seen one!'

. . . water streaming over stone steps, like long tresses, then racing along in veined transparency, with a rippling crescent where it joins the current, a dash of foam jumping with tiny pebbles and twigs losing their bark, effervescent in the sunlight . . .

'I've seen one!'

The other men sat day-dreaming. The one who had brought up the subject seemed to have forgotten his contentious mood. I said nothing and felt that, to them, my silence must resemble the lofty, detached indulgence with which men of science look upon laymen who stumble naïvely into a technical realm. One of the men finally asked me a question, not without a certain timidity.

'Would you know how to build one?'

He did not wait for me to answer. He turned to his companions and pointed out the lack of foresight with which they let the water escape or evaporate during the rainy season. A man with my technical background could plan the construction, supervise the work, and then see to it that the water was distributed fairly.

'Do you think you deserve all that?'

I had risen. I felt wise and powerful, with something radiant inside me. I had been drinking heavily. I started to pace back and forth across the room. The words came easily to me and I could hear my voice stressing each syllable: What would they do with the water?

The fields would become greener, they would be spared from hunger, houses would replace the *cuevas*, a road would be built. But fear would remain, they would go on being servile in the face of power, accepting injustice, taking refuge in bigotry, betraying one another . . . Why had they turned Horqueto over to the police?

Suddenly, out of the blue, I remembered the name of the man who had stabbed his neighbour and who had been lowered into the cistern. Until then I had not bothered to find out the details of the affair, satisfied with what I had picked up in my rare meetings with the people of Elva. However, as I now realized, in the lucidity that comes when one is half-drunk, a kind of anxiety had lingered inside me. Why had Horqueto attacked his neighbour with a knife?

'I'm not interested in politics!' cried the man who had asked for the lace.

He had turned red and was again looking at me with hostility. He and the others, who seemed uncomfortable, had all turned back towards the bar, as though this conversation about sluices and water had never taken place.

I stood there in the middle of the room, defenceless and rather weary. Beyond the windows of the café and the houses in the street, I saw the barren mountains, lit by the rays of the setting sun. I would have given in entirely to melancholy, had I not remembered the water which I now kept hidden in the back of my *cueva*, gleaming like a small glass reliquary, a tabernacle deep in the catacombs, a sheltered, hermetic god.

After dinner, I lingered on in the café. Isabela, her work done, came over and sat down facing me. We were alone. Even the owner had gone upstairs to bed, leaving her to put out the lights and lock up.

My remarks to the other men that evening had made quite an impression on Isabela. She approved of the way I had apparently disdained their offers; this was the proper attitude for someone who was to direct the irrigation project. They would come back to me even more eagerly, more willing to follow my advice. She did not mention my denunciation of cowardice. I was grateful for this; I was no longer so sure of myself.

When, all at once, a gathering of your fellow men turns towards you, as these had done, your faith in Evil is shaken. There are no eyes which do not undermine our belief in darkness. They all send flashes of light ahead, into the night. They do not come towards you; they flee; they wander. But everyone carries his gaze before him in the shadows, like a miner's lamp. The wind from the depths blows everywhere. We grope; we lose one another, we disappear. Soon there will be nothing left.

Soon, there will be nothing left . . . I had felt this when I stood up to the men and criticized the lethargy which made them accomplices to the crimes of our day. But they were also accomplices of this dead earth, of these endless summers, of their own hunger and thirst. Their life was one great conspiracy. Yet it was still life, that stubborn miracle, amidst misery and degradation. Soon, there would be nothing left . . . With her hand, Isabela raised my face to hers.

'I'm coming home with you tonight.'

She, too, had a light in her eyes. I did not have the strength to refuse. We set out for Elva, cutting straight across the mountain. There was a faint moon. The stones rolled from under our feet. Not a single light shone in any direcion, as far as the eye could see. This country had to start from the very beginning.

I bent back the dry bushes for Isabela. Heavy clouds of insects arose, buzzing in the shadows. Isabela's black dress was torn under one arm. When she reached to hold back a branch, I caught a glimpse of that whiter, finer skin where the breast begins. This, too, was why I had agreed to let her come home with me.

I said to myself that there was no danger. The water was hidden behind the curtain. It flowed in a remote corner of my *cueva* where Isabela would have no reason to go. We arrived in Elva towards midnight. A long journey for such brief pleasure! But we were still enough in love to want to wake up next to one another.

Dogs were barking near the empty cistern. They did not forget that one night someone had spoken to them. No one spoke to them now. My key shone in the darkness. I will remember this for a long time. The most trivial details are the hardest to interpret; we die by the light of these brief flashes of memory. I opened the door into the shadows . . . at last! Then I stood motionless on the threshold; I could hear the water.

Only faintly. It was not even a noise; something was moving in the shadows, kept on moving, like the throbbing of blood in one's ears. We went in. I lit a lantern. I turned around to look at Isabela; she did not hear anything. She would have questioned me, or her expression would have betrayed surprise. She was acting quite naturally, and had already thrown herself on the bed. She spent little time undressing; she was probably used to sleeping with her clothes on.

For a moment we were preoccupied with pleasure. I had put out the light. Everything was dark. Then once again, with my head turned slightly towards the back of the *cueva*, I caught the very light, slippery sound, the almost imperceptible murmur, which had been drowned out by our mingled breathing. Isabela was already asleep. I tried to keep awake. What if she got up, without my hearing her, in the middle of the night? I moved the lantern away, so that she would not be able to find it, and drifted into semi-consciousness.

Men from the village were passing by, holding large triangles of slate under their arms. What were they going to build? The slate was a pleasing colour; a smoky black. The prow of a large, dark ship, in the port of Santander, one winter night, many years ago. She was sailing for some Scandinavian port: Möv, Löx . . . I could not remember the name . . . Rør . . . ? Isabela cried out. I woke up. I touched her. She was sitting up and asking for the lantern. I lit it.

'I didn't know where I was.'

She held her hand to her brow, rose, and took a few steps, like someone trying to get his bearings. Her fingers ran along a ledge in the clay wall. With her fingernail, she pried off a few flecks of mica. I asked her to come back to bed. She did not answer. She stood slightly beyond the threshold of the alcove where my bed lay, staring to the right. What could she see? That part of the *cueva* was completely dark.

'What is the white curtain doing back there?'

She turned around and looked at me. She seemed worried. I was sorry I had used such a light piece of material to hide the water. Of course it was the only piece I had. I told Isabela that the curtain covered a storeroom where I kept supplies.

'But it's moving!'

I tried to laugh. But I grew worried. I got up. Could the coolness of the water have created a draught in the close atmosphere of the *cueva*? It had been hot for so long, the sun so relentless, the earth so deeply scorched . . . Could the coldness of the water become a live, tangible presence, could the coldness of the water become a spirit, a transparent divinity ready to issue forth and animate this world smothered by the dust of mountains and plains, eroded by loneliness?

I took Isabela by the arm and leaned into the shadows. I could not tell whether the curtain was moving; all I could make out was a pale blur. I was silent a moment too long. Isabela pulled her arm away and went back to bed. I followed her. My expression had probably betrayed my anxiety. Any other man would have put an end to Isabela's fears by holding her tight, grabbing the lamp, carrying it into the alcove, and then lifting the curtain on a pile of old tyres, worn and whitened, or couplings caked with grease.

But imagine revealing water, laying it bare as it streamed down the earthen wall, or spurted feebly – I no longer knew, I hadn't seen it since morning – a sight as staggering as a fresh corpse! . . . Isabela was lying on the bed with her eyes wide open. I lay down next to her.

'Don't put out the light.'

She was looking at the low curve of the ceiling overhead, where flecks of mica sparkled in the dark clay.

'Why do you defend Horqueto?'

It was true; I did defend him. Without admitting it to myself, I had been defending him ever since he had been lowered into the cistern. But it was not until that evening in the café that I had uttered his name aloud.

'I think the other man informed on him. He was taking revenge.'

'Was he a friend of yours?'

No, he was not a friend of mine. In a crowd, I might not even be able to pick out his face. And yet, behind his surly expression, his fleshy exterior, his drunkenness, there was something which 'spoke to me'.

'When I was a little girl – right after the civil war – people used to say that there were underground caverns around here, full of armed men.'

Isabela was staring at me. I shook my head: absurd tales. She lay thoughtful for a long time.

'Now you can put the light out.'

I did. She kept still. I could sense that she was listening in the darkness. I did not dare make the slightest move. I was listening to the water, and carried away by this faint sound, which I alone could hear, my imagination led me deep into the black labyrinth where the shadow armies of Spain had been keeping watch for years, invisible men, entrenched behind hidden springs.

We left again well before dawn. Isabela was afraid of meeting one of the inhabitants of Elva. Weary after a sleepless night, we were sparing with words. We parted in front of my shop. Isabela did not have far to go to town.

'Don't tell anyone that I came to your place.'

I promised. She asked me to swear on it, and I did. Then she hurried down the lonely road. The sun, now rising behind the hills, would soon bring a torrid whiteness back to this road on which nothing appeared for hour after hour. Today, there would only be the figure of Isabela, with her dress torn under her arm, walking away, never to return.

I knew that she had found out everything about me. The bitterness which I could not shed, the need for justice, which in this country is known as Evil, the love, which in this country can compromise a man. She had not understood what had frightened her in the *cueva*, but she knew that I was at the root of her fears. Now she retreated.

For years, Spain has been retreating from me. The dazzling roads are still there, stretching out as far as the eye can see, the ochre plains striped with rods of shadow, the mountains which the sun transforms into blue flames will always be there in the distance, but my true country has gone, gone forever, in spite of the mirages of olive trees, of corn and vines. Like the sea, which gives and then takes away, my country is here, but is not here. I am not the only one to feel its absence. It can be read on the lips of men, in the eyes of children, a race of men absent from themselves.

I continued to work every day, or at least pretended to. I refurbished useless casings, the way idle women refurbish kettles. Well before noon, the heat would become unbearable. I suffocated in my black, grease-stained shed. Rays of fire shot through the ill-fitting planks.

Sometimes a motorist who had lost his way, or was worried that his engine might boil over, would knock at the shutters. I started; they had come to arrest me. My heart beat, with both joy and anguish. I felt rich in guilt. My crime was paltry, to be sure, nothing the police could prosecute. Hiding a spring! But for me the spring was a weapon. If I was arrested, I would reveal everything that lay behind it: my armies, my revenge, this onslaught, this hue-and-cry upon Spain, all loyalties severed, and I would tell them, I would tell them . . .

I went out into the sun, flushed, perspiring, almost staggering. An insignificant-looking man was standing there, shading his right temple with his hand. The countryside was deserted, with a bluish haze for miles around. I put oil and gasoline in his car. Water? No, I had none. As I worked, the man made nasty remarks to me: a garage without water! I answered him caustically. I swept my arm through space: the mantle of God, yes, of course, but moth-eaten with light. What did he expect, that faceless little man, no doubt an insurance salesman from Murcia? If you choose to live in a place, you bring your own water!

He left, disgruntled, in a cloud of dust. I went back into my cave, with its velvety, grease-stained walls. Into deepest solitude. My life no longer had any meaning. Later on, I would return along the dirt road, in the paths of Visigoths and Moors with their patience-worn faces, to my *cueva* where threads of water tangled in the shadows, and then ran off into a cleft. Interminably.

I had already begun to tire of this continuity. I had enjoyed the sudden discovery of water, gleaming like my private treasure, like a secret weapon, but the time had come for this treasure, this weapon, to disappear. The knife which will be used one day, perhaps that very night, usually sleeps in a pocket, a drawer, in the back of a room, behind a stone, or under the floor. But suppose that it did not sleep, suppose that the blade kept flashing, making furtive noises, like a slithering serpent! . . . Then the murder which you are contemplating becomes a haemorrhage. Your own. The blade keeps moving, growing longer, sharper, until you finally slip into it.

I was slipping into the spring. It drew me into the black veins of the earth, even further than death. At times, carried along by this slow overflow, I even forgot my original intention. I lost my way, as though, absorbed from all sides, exactly like the water, I had been sucked into the earth, without being able to reach the secret *cueva*, the nest of captive shadows where, for a hundred years, for twenty-five years, ever since the death of Horqueto, my brothers-in-arms had been standing waiting for me.

In the end, I had to realize that I was alone, in all of Spain. Tomorrow I would reveal the water. I would go that far. Laughing children would splash in the sunshine. Life would go on; a respite amidst hate and injustice.

One evening I went back into town, to see Isabela. I knew, too, that I would come to love her. There were a few men in the café. They greeted me but seemed less cordial than usual. I sat down at one of the tables. Isabela waited on me, said good evening with a smile, but then disappeared again quickly, saying she was overwhelmed with chores that evening.

I saw her hurry back and forth across the room several times. Her face was tense now, and she sent darting glances in my direction, frowning as though in pain, as though she wanted to convey something which she could not express otherwise. I noticed that he dress had been mended beneath her arm.

At the bar, the men stood with their backs to me, talking in low voices. I looked at the posters on the wall. One of them announced a bullfight that was coming soon: the most absurd of all the faces of Spain. It would never disappear. Wars could break out, injustice run rampant, hunger and thirst could reign, but late Sunday afternoon, there would always be pools of black blood in the arena. If folklore is to continue hiding reality, if passion is to win out over conscience, they must be fed with cruelty and madness. The bulls have become Spain's best soldiers. Not my Spain; the town where the bullfight was to take place was the one where Horqueto was imprisoned.

Once again, Isabela crossed the room. She disappeared into a little vestibule at the foot of the stairs. I rose and followed her. She started up the steps, then saw me and stopped. I caught up with her. The light in the hall was very dim. Isabela touched my arm.

'You have to get away from here. As far as you possibly can. Tonight. Now go back downstairs, quickly.'

But why should I go away? She leapt up a few more steps.

'They talked to the priest.'

She fled to the landing, where she turned out the light. She waited. I could picture her, rigid in the shadows.

'Will you write me?'

I did not answer.

'Later on, maybe I'll try to join you.'

I waited before answering.

'I'll write you.'

I went back down into the café. It was empty. All the men had left. The owner was dozing. I left some money on the table and started back to Elva, over the mountain. I could guess the reason for Isabela's warning. I had said too much the Sunday before; they might have thought I was preaching revolt. I was already considered a heathen. And in this country, from that moment on, guilt stalks one's every step.

But they had made it irresistible. I would try to build up my guilt. It was the only thing that was fertile in this country. I would have to go away, however, so that they would not deprive me of it too quickly, with their punishments. I would go away. I would slip along in the shadows. I would live in crowded parts of the city, where the streets are narrow and winding. At night, I would hear men shouting and fighting beneath my window. There would be a harbour full of sunshine, reflections, smells, and the fluttering shadows of laundry. My guilt would grow in wisdom. I would drink, make love to girls against the edge of tables; I would steal. In secret, with others like me, I would prepare for the night when trails of fire would streak across the monotonous, empty skies of this country.

Carried along by my new exhilaration – tomorrow, escape,

all that freedom gained through error, tomorrow, the hulls of ships, the slate grey tint of the sunshine, of the darkness, of the winter, all this waiting for me, tomorrow – I quickly reached the outskirts of Elva. Soon I would leave this dry land.

I cut across the fields. Dead plants crackled beneath my feet. Pungent dust, still warm from the day, rose from the earth. Tomorrow, the seacoasts of Spain, tomorrow, the whistle of steamships, the living streets . . . I stopped. My feet sank into some loose earth. I could feel a coolness about my ankles, the touch of leaves. What kind of illusions still hung on?

I leaned over and pulled up handfuls of plants, plants with a faintly bitter smell: herbs, nightshade, milkweed, greener than any I had ever seen, succulent, stiff with sap, their veins black in the moonlight. I tore them apart and let the shreds fall at my feet. But as soon as I dropped them, I wanted to plunge my hands back into this vegetation which had burst forth so luxuriantly after months of drought and frustrated wrath.

I crouched down and again tore out handfuls of herbs and leaves. I crushed them, smelled them and then threw them away as soon as they had lost their freshness. Then I reached back for more handfuls. Before me, the knoll which held my *cueva* stood out like a black dome against the whiteness of the moon.

I stood up and walked towards the shadow of the knoll. Then it was night again. But still the vegetation continued. I bent over to pick some leaves. They seemed broader and heavier. In the darkness, I could not identify them. Solanum, perhaps. I repeated this name, as though it would reveal a secret which had been weighing on me for months, as though it were the key to the enigma which I found everywhere, in this country devoured by light.

Once again, I ran my hands through the cool plants. Yes, Solanum, no doubt, Euphorbium, Ocimum, without meaning anything precise to me, these words had remained in my mind, from an old botany text which I sometimes read inside my *cueva*, when all around me the world was on fire. Solanum: perhaps with this everything would be explained . . .

It was then that they sprang on me. They must have been hiding in the shadows. I recognized the man who had asked for the lace. I did not know the names of the three others. They led me round to the front of my *cueva*. They questioned me: what kind of sorcery was I practising? What was this green field behind my knoll, and why was I there, on my knees, pulling up plants?

Suddenly, I understood: the water which welled up inside my *cueva* and then disappeared into a cleft probably sank into the ground behind the knoll and fertilized the abandoned field. I explained this to the men. One of them raised his hand to slap me in the face. The others held him back. They asked for my key, and when I had given it to them, led me to the cistern. They lowered me into it without difficulty, by passing a rope under my arms. I helped them. Moonlight shone into the cistern, illuminating half the interior. I saw the footprints which Horqueto had left.

Then they went away again. From time to time, the dogs barked. I sat down and watched the shadows creeping across the cistern floor. Tomorrow, the police, and a prison cell . . . But the police never came.

Towards noon today, as I dozed in the heat, with my jacket over my head, some men lowered a basket, with bread, wine, and a melon. There was a note pinned to it. They needed more 'sluices'. If I would work for them, with them, everything would be forgotten. The word 'everything' was underlined.

I tore up the note, ate the bread and melon, and drank the wine. I was laughing. I am still laughing, this evening, while the dogs bark and the sweat of the day dries upon me. I can feel silence all around, the silence of Elva, waiting in tense anticipation for a single word from me. I feel calm and strong, the way a god must feel, I imagine.

Tomorrow I shall climb out of the cistern. I shall work with them. Perhaps they have suffered enough now to join me in my search for justice, that hidden sluice which we will break

open together, so that it can finally flow over all of Spain . . .
I just saw a shadow crossing the moon. It must not rain before
our day of wrath!

translated by Merloyd Lawrence

The Blind Men
of St Xavier

Now that it is all so far away they seem to swim up into my memory, through that rainy winter, as though out of the ocean deeps, with arms that move like seaweed, I see them now, groping their way more anxiously through space, more hopelessly crippled by darkness than they ever were; reduced to the very symbol of blindness, endlessly parting the massed shadows that their dead eyes, and the weight of the past, accumulate before them today.

Time has gone by, and now I see them and myself delivered to boundless sorrow; I see them newly blinded, stretching out their arms in the endless anguish of dark night, and myself standing there once more, watching them come, to the point of terror . . . In the days when I used to meet them they were staid of bearing, sparse of gesture. Slowly they made their way from the far end of the avenue, walking a little stiffly out of caution, with their white sticks tapping the pavement before them. The intent look on their faces and their meticulous gait made them seem like accountants taking stock of space, step by step.

Their movements expressed only vigilant calm and the confidence that, every instant, they gained afresh. Then they would linger, touching with the tips of their sticks the corner or the step they had recognized, stroking it affectionately; their life and their happiness lay in such recognition.

Their humility was deceptive; though they walked so slowly, so meekly, hugging the walls, they soon came to represent for me something that moved inexorably forward, something whose timid, patiently groping gestures must inevitably annex all that came within its reach. Sometimes when one of the blind men passed I closed my eyes, and I recognized that obstinate tapping sound of a blind man's stick; it was the sound that fate makes in one's life.

I used to see the blind men of St Xavier at the place where Cécile and I met every day. They lived in a home nearby; they made brushes of a simple sort and played the harmonium. Towards evening the door was opened for them by nuns, and one by one they went out to walk in the neighbourhood, tapping the asphalt with their sticks and lighting their way with a smile amidst the anxious darkness of the crowd.

That priestlike smile . . . It counteracted, for a brief instant, the ominous character of the blind men's appearance, at the corner of the two streets or along the endless vista of the avenue, every evening at nightfall. And yet its constancy was disquieting to me. It seemed unalterable. Often the rain was falling or a cold wind was blowing in the avenue. But what did the weather matter to the blind men? Wind, fog or mild breeze, for them the weather was always a sea which they knew only by its breath.

And it was along the shores of that sea, from which rugged walls separated them, that they resumed their walk every evening, walking in a different world from ours, along some protected pier, while the sound of the city, like the sound of the sea, swelled around them intermittently. And they would walk straight at you, smiling as if they had seen you, and had seen not only your outward shape but also your kindheartedness, your innocence, a whole reassuring world of thoughts towards which they stretched out their veined, trembling hands. Then I would draw aside. The tapping noise would move away into the distance, opening a leper's path into the night.

Cécile was always late coming, and there was something threatening about her lateness. She was married and lived in an atmosphere of lies. She dreaded night, when the married couple were left alone together again, inescapably reunited, brooding over her unkindness. Suppose all of a sudden, behind the silence, behind the words, the truth should appear, like a familiar face unexpectedly seen in a crowd?

I was there at the corner of the two streets, against the wall, sheltering from the rain, and I was afraid. From time to time a blind man turned the corner, feeling the wall, his face uplifted and smiling. I would draw back a few steps. The blind man would go on walking in the darkness with his relentlessly slow gait and his smile.

It was almost always the same blind man who came round the street corner where I stood; his hours were as regular as mine. He came just as anxiety was beginning to overwhelm me and his appearance flung me on to a steeper slope of darkness, opening over gulfs, as when one has left behind some ominous landmark, some moonlit stone calvary.

The blind man belonged to those nocturnal auguries, difficult to identify, that mark the threshold of one's downfall: the lonely yew tree on the hill, the place where four roads meet, the broken milestone, the strange beggar; ancient symbols of a summons you have five or six chances to obey, failing which you must die.

I was not to die that evening, for Cécile appeared at last. She was still speechless with haste. She took me by the arm and we went off down the dark avenue, where, after a few steps, we kissed with rain on our mouths. Near us a blind man was tapping his way through the night.

'He was there already,' Cécile said, meaning her husband. We never referred to him except by that word, which implied a burdensome and hated otherness. The word was equivalent to a murder; it showed me the man from behind.

We walked round the houses, in the anguish of our nocturnal love. When I left Cécile at the street corner where I had met her, the blind men were already gone . . .

One evening when I was waiting at the usual place the blind man whom I often saw came up to the edge of the pavement to cross the street. He seemed to hesitate. I took him by the arm and led him over to the other side. As we went he talked about the rain. I complained of it too, out of politeness, and then, letting him go, I came back to the place where I had stood a few minutes before. And then it all began again . . . the nightly slow parade of the blind men, holding out their sticks, carved out of hospital wood, walking through darkness, through the sea air, those dead smiling faces uplifted towards invisible sea gulls, the cautious sauntering along the Parisian ramparts of those who had retired from sight.

Sometimes when the rain grew fiercer Cécile and I took refuge in a nearby café. There we found the blind men again, also driven in by the rain. They sat, usually in pairs, on benches, their sightless gaze fixed in front of them, reciting.

Their conversation was like a liturgy, full of repetitions and of responses rather than answers; it lacked the significance that a live darting glance would have given it. Blindness conferred on it the fixed character of a rite; there was a rigid bareness about their speech. We used to kiss in front of them, and their eyes were like those amber or opal beads of the necklace that my fingers played with while I kissed.

And under that lustreless gaze I felt like a wanderer. The blind men were suppressed witnesses who saved me from solitude and peopled the night with which they surrounded our love. This night with its fringe of beings that were still human seemed to grant consent. We passed in front of the blind men and in their sightlessness I read my pardon.

It was only outside, when they sought their way along the street with tapping sticks, that they took on prophetic airs, assumed the relentless groping gait of Destiny, with their white sticks held out obliquely, rigidly into the night. The obstinate tapping of the sticks became the very pulse of the earth, became the knocking at a door that would not open, or that might open one day: a muffled message to the immured.

It was not too late but soon it would be too late. Too late for what? Their colourless faces expressed only a commonplace appeal to bear one's cross with patience, a message of charity, smiling innocence, faith in God, And I should have immediately averted my eyes had I not guessed, from listening to them, from watching them come irresistible and groping in the night, that their message was greater than they.

Another evening the blind man who usually came up while I was waiting at the street corner wanted to cross the street again, and I helped him. Other passers-by were ready to take his arm as he stood hesitating at the edge of the pavement, but I had hurried forward. I wanted to get close to the blind man to convince myself of his insignificance. Everything seemed to confirm this: the stiff grey ready-made suit, the thick hands, the water-sleeked hair. I grasped his arm. Some cars were passing. I told him we must wait. No doubt he recognized my voice.

'I know you,' he said. 'You helped me to cross once before, not long ago.'

I noticed that he was blinking. And yet when he had passed near me his sightless eyes had worn a fixed stare. As he surrendered himself into my power to cross the street, above all as he ventured on to that uncertain ford that our common experience set between us, he wanted no doubt to arm himself with all the force of his blindness, with all the black, massive faith that dwelt in him.

He had a smooth, ordinary face. Drops of rain were shining on his cheeks. I told him that it was indeed I who had helped him cross the street a few days earlier.

'Are you always here, then?' he asked.

He was smiling, his eyes tightly closed now. Our two meetings were hardly enough to justify this obviously ironical question. Perhaps on other evenings he had guessed at my presence as I moved away from the wall to let him pass; perhaps he had felt me living through that voiceless whispering that betrays a human being in the silence, his breathing, the imperceptible movements of his body in its clothes, the endless attrition of immobility, all that which, in the darkness, transforms a man who is standing silent and holding his breath into a rustle of shifting sand . . . I thought myself discovered. I replied that I was in fact there most evenings.

'I bet you're waiting for a woman,' the blind man said to me in a tone of low connivance that implied a nudge and a wink.

I did not want to answer him, but fearing lest he should mistake my silence for embarrassment and wishing to pay him back with his own insolence I replied that, really, it was impossible to hide anything from him. He seemed insensitive to the cruelty of this remark, and seeing in it no doubt only a tribute to his powers of divination he began to laugh. I dropped his arm. He ceased laughing and thanked me; then, recovering his rigidity like a soldier when he starts marching again, he moved slowly away, his stick tapping the ground in front of him.

It was about that time that we experienced, Cécile and I, the keenest anguish. There was apparently nothing to justify it; Cécile's husband had made no complaints and nothing suggested that suspicion had been awakened in his mind. But his unawareness took on a strange colour at times. There dawned in his eye a look of sadness, a mute, puzzled panic; it was like the terrified amazement of a man being murdered in his sleep, who feels himself pierced by pain and death before having shed his trustfulness.

That wan mask forced on the face of innocence by so cruel and murderous an awakening pursued us as we walked among the houses, in the darkness, desperately using the last minutes allotted by our daily lies.

'Now I must go back,' Cécile would say, 'he wouldn't understand. No, be reasonable, I must go back.'

Pulling up the collar of her coat, she went off again towards the lighted home where a man sat wondering why he wanted to cry. I watched her go away in a sort of terror. I was afraid lest she should take pity on that man or else, anxious to perfect her lie and yielding to that happy endurance of love that sometimes, in a woman, outlives love itself, she might that evening no longer deny herself to him. The thought made my head reel.

Next evening I was at the street corner before the time set for our meeting. It seemed to me that in this way the moment I had waited for all day was already granted to me, and that the happiness I was to enjoy when Cécile should come at last would spill over on to the waiting period, like the light from a hidden moon.

Being there cured me of my doubts, too, proved to me that I was loved. And on my worst evenings I used to think that if I, in turn, were betrayed by Cécile, I might by coming earlier surprise her in the street with her husband and discover from their attitude what their relations were.

On these worst evenings the blind man whom I knew and all the other blind men who were walking about in the darkness seemed deliberately to exaggerate: they were slower and more punctual than ever, stiffer in their bearing, tapping the ground ever more sonorously as though in some incantatory rite. And they smiled more, too. As they turned the street corner they stroked the wall with so light a hand that when they moved away from it the houses they had touched seemed to sway slowly like a ship leaving the quayside. So sure of themselves, so obscurely prophetic with their congealed stare amidst the glistening city rain!

My blind man smiled even more than the others when he passed near me. He must have felt my presence. I was so sure of this that I was embarrassed; it seemed as if I ought to greet him. Then Cécile came, rather pale as usual from hurrying. I questioned her wildly: how was he, what had he said, what had he done?

'He's unhappy,' Cécile answered, 'I know now that he's unhappy . . .'

I rejected all pity; why, weren't we all unhappy? Why should he have been spared? He was in love; had he thought he would have to accept only his own love? But when you love you always have to accept the whole of love, and admit the love that will break your heart. I deafened myself with arguments but drew no answer from Cécile. Then at last I fell silent and through the silence, broken only by the drip from the dead trees along the avenue, his suffering seemed audible.

. . . A little later I once again helped my blind man to cross the street.

I had long ago decided I would leave that task to someone else. But that evening there was nobody else on the pavement when the blind man came up to the edge of it. At first I stood motionless against the wall. Across the street, some passers-by were looking at me. Then I felt ashamed. I went forward and took the blind man's arm. As soon as I touched him he closed his eyes and began to laugh; he had recognized me.

'Oh, this time it's you all right,' he said as he waited for the stream of cars to go by. 'Would you believe it, I made a mistake the other evening. Although it happened at the corner of the other street I could have sworn it was you. It was just at the same time, and everything else about it was just the same, I swear to you; the same way of holding me by the arm, the same way of walking, the same . . . I don't know how to explain, the same trace of a woman's scent. You'll maybe tell me that many woman use the same scent, but nobody but myself would recognize this scent on you – just the faintest trace of it, and it's very special to her, no doubt, and to you. In any case I wonder if it's not just an illusion on my part, and if I've unintentionally said "scent" when I meant something else . . . No, after all, it's not so much the scent; that might be a coincidence, probably is. No, you see, it's everything else besides the scent that's so hard to explain. Shall I tell you what I think? It's the same sort of sadness, as if you were both in the same boat! That's it . . . When the other chap spoke, after helping me across, I realized that of course it wasn't you and that I'd been wrong. And yet perhaps I hadn't been as wrong as all that ...'

We had come to the other side of the street but I did not let go of the blind man. He turned his lifeless, smiling face to me and then, alarmed no doubt at feeling himself still grasped firmly by the arm although we were already standing on the opposite pavement, he stopped smiling.

I wanted to ask him more questions. Was he lying? But why should he lie? An absurd curiosity possessed me about that shadowy double of mine of whom he had just been speaking, this man who had the same aura of sadness as myself, who haunted the district and gave his arm to blind men as I did. I was thinking of Cécile's husband. I was about to ask the blind man whether the man who had helped him to cross had seemed tall, whether he spoke with a peculiar accent, when it struck me that I should make a fool of myself. I dropped the blind man's arm. He began to smile again but, still somewhat disconcerted, he moved away rather more quickly than usual and without thanking me.

I was left strangely disturbed by the blind man's words. Normally they would have left my mind untroubled but too many evenings spent waiting, surrounded by the blind, surrounded by obscure omens, in the anguish of a secret love, had predisposed my mind to extravagant thoughts.

Without being really aware of it, I had been waiting for a message, a sign, from those who came upon me in the night, heralded by the patient tap of a stick; I had been waiting for a judgment from the blind men, from passers-by, from all and sundry and from heaven itself. And the judgment had come. True, its form was still sibylline; neither the culprit nor the victim was named, but it was revealed to me that they were alike, that nothing distinguished them from one another in the depths of night, that their sufferings were equal and their chances equal and that, hidden in real darkness, they had become identified in blind brotherhood.

As soon as Cécile stood beside me I repeated the blind man's words to her. She seemed at first to pay little heed to them, then, seeing my disquiet, she grew thoughtful.

'But then,' she murmured, 'if he had been so close to him at the very moment when we met, he must have been watching us! And even if he was not watching us he must have seen us together, for he must have gone up the avenue after leaving the blind man . . . Wait: just when we were kissing, perhaps, and without our seeing him, we . . .'

I brushed aside her fears. I had not shared them for a moment. Nothing seemed to justify them; if he had caught sight of us together that evening, Cécile's husband would surely not have withdrawn into silence.

'Who knows?' said Cécile. 'Perhaps he thinks that by waiting patiently he will win . . .'

This answer implied that our chances might be equal. Since Cécile had begun to speak I had realized that they were indeed equal. Cécile showed no surprise that her husband and I weighed the same in the blind man's scales, that to the blind man the same grief and the same scent hung about us both, that to his secret senses we seemed to speak the same language, with the same number of words, were scarred with the same wounds and loaded with the same gifts . . . To be so like me, this man must surely have received as much as I!

But while I tortured myself thus I blamed myself for lack of faith. Perhaps, long after he has ceased to be loved, a man retains the imprint of the woman who has loved him, like some physical memory or waking dream; he still echoes the accents of the now distant country where he was once welcome, now revived by his nostalgia . . . But really, I told myself, all such thoughts were absurd. The blind man might have been misled by his imagination or deceived by a mere likeness. I asked Cécile to question her husband cunningly to try and discover if he had, one evening, helped the blind man to cross the street. She did not refuse. She was anxious to know whether her husband had seen us together that evening.

2*

The answer she brought me next day left me still uncertain. She had spoken to him of the blind men, of how many there were, and how regularly they took their walk along the street each evening. She had expressed her pity for them. Her husband had nodded, and answered merely with a few obscure muttered words. What had he said? She could not remember. I begged her to make an effort, to search her memory once more.

'It's ridiculous,' she kept saying. 'I wanted to remember his exact words and I've quite forgotten them. However, they wouldn't have told us anything.'

I was angry with her for forgetting ; it seemed to me suspicious. I wanted to know those words. Their very obscurity made them important to me; it might reveal that this man too, through contact with the blind, had found his way into that strange world of second sight and hitherto secret correspondences. I reproached Cécile for her thoughtlessness and frivolity; it was the first time I had spoken harshly to her.

We were walking in the darkness more swiftly than usual. A few blind men passed alongside the walls, smiling, rigid, rather pale. It struck me that I had not seen my familiar blind man that evening, and this absence worried me, without my knowing why. What right had I to scold Cécile? I had not even had the presence of mind to ask the blind man, last night, if he had spoken to the man who resembled me so closely and explained the mistake he had made. If he had said nothing, why should Cécile's husband have remembered anything about so commonplace an encounter?

Next day I kept watch for the blind man, to question him. I did not see him come; nor the following evening either. I had stopped talking to Cécile about the blind man. But the husband still existed; he slept badly, spoke little, gazed sadly at Cécile. He behaved almost as if he were being given a daily dose of arsenic. It seemed to me unfair of him to suffer so. I hated him for suffering . . . At last one evening I recognized my blind man on the other side of the avenue. He had changed his route.

I hurried towards him and walked by his side as far as the
street he had to cross. Then I took him by the arm. He gave a
start of surprise, then yielded and let himself be guided. He
was not smiling and walked in silence. I reminded him of what
he had told me a few days earlier. Had he mentioned our likeness to the man who had helped him to cross the street?

'Did I mention it to him?' said the blind man. 'Yes, certainly,
it was so strange, so very striking. Do you think I shouldn't
have? . . . Yes, you're right, I shouldn't have, and I shouldn't
have mentioned it to you either. That occurred to me too late –
the night when he came to ask me questions, just as you're
doing tonight. He wanted me to show him the place where I
met you. I refused, of course; and do you know what
happened?'

We had long since crossed the street. I had let go of the
blind man's arm. Feeling someone by his side who could point
out obstacles, the blind man walked rather fast, with his stick
raised; he dragged me after him. Cécile must be waiting for me
already. I seized the blind man by the arm to stop him. He
broke away from me.

'No, let's keep walking,' he said, 'let's get away from here. I
don't want to be seen with you. I don't want to be involved in
it all any more. I want to stay neutral, as they say. Neutral,
d'you hear? Neither on one side nor on the other. How could
I choose, in any case? You're both so alike, it's confusing and
ridiculous, and so . . . What happened?' he went on, as I
reminded him of his original remark. 'It was quite simple; he
followed me. Until this evening. The first evening I thought
it was you! Those steps behind me! I stopped; he stopped. I
thought it was you and I couldn't understand, and then it
occurred to me that it must be him. When I had to cross a street,
he'd fall behind so as not to have to help me and so betray
himself. Afterwards, there he was behind me again. I'd have
liked to go up to him and tell him to leave me in peace. At one
point I turned round and waved my stick at him impatiently
like this, in the dark: "Go away, go away!" But d'you think he

took any notice of it? He didn't leave me alone till I got back to the Home.

'And the same thing happened every evening. Of course when I knew it was him I took a different route. He obviously wanted to know who you were, and if we had gone past where you were he'd have made no mistake, you can be sure. There aren't so many people crazy enough to stand waiting at the street corner every night in the rain. And besides, other people are bound to notice that likeness too . . . No, don't worry, he's not here tonight. It's you who are here. That's the way things are . . . Do you know him, by the way?'

I did not know him. I had never seen him, but now he was as familiar to me as a brother, a faraway brother, his image somewhat blurred by absence. Cécile had told me so much about him, about his sad eyes and his unhappiness and his pallor, that I seemed to see him through dark, swift-flowing water, in the glitter and confusion of the current, like a drowned man with a white imploring face.

'No, I don't know him,' I told the blind man, 'but I almost feel as if I could recognize him now.'

'Yes, indeed!' cried the blind man with a sort of jubilation. 'You could recognize him without ever having seen him. And that's what matters. It's reassuring to see; it satisfies you. People's appearances make a sort of screen between what they really are and yourself. And you feel so sheltered with that screen in front of you!

'You know I haven't always been blind, and if I have lost daylight as a result of my accident, I've found another kind of light. No, everything isn't as dark as you'd think. People that you don't see still cast a shadow. Just as they always did; only before, one wasn't conscious of the weight of shadows. Now, that man was casting a shadow in your life. Soon he'll cease to do so. I've got a feeling that everything is going to be brought back into order once more. He didn't follow me this evening. Just now, when you came up to me and I realized it was you, I understood . . .'

He had regained all his self-confidence, and was striding along beside me, grasping his white stick by the middle, and I noticed that in his moment of triumph he mimicked the bearing of those that see. For he was triumphant. He had guessed at my distress and at that of Cécile's husband. He had connected them, he had merged them together; he patched up the unseen, he reshaped darkness. But what had he 'understood'? Why did he say he had understood? I suddenly felt more horribly distressed than ever. I left the blind man hurriedly. He seemed surprised, and stood motionless, shouting after me: 'You'll tell me, all the same! You'll tell me!'

I despised him. I blamed myself for having thought of him as a prophet. True prophets are indifferent to what is to come. It was late; I was a long way from the place where Cécile would be waiting for me. I ran. She was not there.

I began to hurry through the neighbouring streets, endlessly going over the same ground that we used to cover together. I knew now that Cécile would never come back, that I would do nothing to see her again and that I wanted to drain it all to the utmost – the night and the rain and the place, henceforward firmly anchored in my memory, in which our love still seemed to linger alive, amidst the bewilderment of its sudden end.

Other men were coming towards me or against me, driven by the same haste, and I watched them come, expecting each of them to reveal the tortured brother's face of the man to whom my love and my unhappiness bound me forever, in that deep darkness where, behind the illusion of consciousness and the vivid light of day, we all walk with staring eyes, like blind men.

translated by Jean Stewart

Marble

THESE LIGHT patches, along the side of the mountain, could be seen from miles around, like chalky landslides cut through the dark vegetation, the mingled pine and ilex which grew even on the bare outcroppings of rock, along with brambles, mastic, and strange plants veined in blood, shrubs of a thousand different species beneath which a pool of night lingered on, even at high noon when nothing survived but the buzz of an insect.

These paler cliffs, almost always under the summit, suggested landslides which crumble mountains, avalanches of rusty rock and sand which hollow deep ravines overhung with saplings, tufts of grass, their roots in midair like aerial plants, which suck their life from the wind. Frozen disasters, adding a note of dramatic hazard to the natural majesty of the landscape, evidence of underground forces, of storms, reminders of the dark history within this sun-drenched mountain, the same history, without a beginning or an end, that lay beneath the thousands of bushes, nests of darkness brooding upon a deeper shade than the windswept, light-riddled trees, sentinels on the horizon.

The mountain was no longer a simple, radiant peak over-looking the fields, hazy blue in the heat, and the sea. It was a blind face with a thousand introspective eyes, a power asleep in the black grip of the brambles, of the trees felled by avalanches of earth. These trees, buried alive at the bottom of ravines, weighed down by a flock of stone birds which had descended upon them by night, did not die, they moved into a new realm; their reptilian branches penetrated in all directions; their buds turned black like dormant larvae; their leaves clung to the rocks like undersea creatures, and later on, imprinted themselves upon it.

Fossils are the coins of the night, medals struck in the realm of darkness. People would sometimes climb down into the ravines to examine the stones brought to light by the landslides and find effigies of the vegetable or marine universe that lay hidden within the mountain: shells, star shapes, and striations, and, even as they turned the rocks over, the thin, laminated shadow on which they rested fled like a lizard, vanished like a black puddle siphoned away at a single draught. Then they discovered that darkness existed, was alive.

Reality does not wear the clear, luminous expression ascribed to it; it wears a black patch over one eye. Even here, even in the Mediterranean sunshine. One had to leave these ravines, and cross over the ridge, to reach the marble quarries which looked like light patches on the mountain, when seen from afar, by anyone coming from the sea.

On this side the marble formed a solid, unflawed pediment, bare in places. The relief of its rough outcroppings was blurred by clay left by the rains. It gave the mountain a dry and stub-born, but reassuring appearance. Here there was no room for darkness. Marble sealed off the mountain.

In the quarries, however, geology gave way to the architec-ture of buried palaces. The incisions made by dynamite and picks revealed walls, terraces, and steps, as though an immense edifice had been excavated, an edifice without doors or windows, apparently solid, without rooms or any interior space, unless, one day, deep within the thickness of the walls, as though in the heart of a pyramid, a narrow chamber should be discovered, more airtight than death itself, a vacuum of darkness, useless, serving only to marshal about itself, in ramparts, bastions, and buttresses, this absolute mass of marble. A castle that was new and intact, for the cutting rid the marble of all signs of wear, of its patina, brought back the colour and grain; a castle that was never finished, more real, more exact every day, but at the same time receding, fleeing before you, unveiling only its outermost fortifications, and behind them, still more fortifications, as the marble walls crumbled on the din of an always victorious, always futile siege.

The gash in the mountainside grew wider, once again leaving grasses hanging over the edge, bushes feeding on the wind, plants repeating themselves in their dishevelled roots, like those which grow in water.

Granular and as if frosted by the slow crystallization of the lime, the stone at the face of the quarry seemed natural, presented the true appearance of marble, although it had been laid bare by dynamite and pickaxe. The chill that inhabited it was dispersed by this roughness, the slow bite of the lime beneath one's hand. It would be restored by polishing down in the valley, a process that was carried almost to the point of vitrification.

From then on, the marble found itself enclosed in transparency. The pattern of its mutilation adhered to this as closely as tissue to a laboratory slide. With its veins, its capillaries, its often vivid colouring, it was like a smooth cross-section of living flesh, preserved forever.

And so the marble was transfigured. As a result of the polishing, each piece, according to its complexion, portrayed a kind of petrified landscape, with sunrises, sunsets, cloud formations, always under the same solemn illumination, while the mountain and everything upon it remained subject to the seasons, to a confusion of light and shadow, beneath fluctuating, uncertain skies.

There, in this contrast, royalty became evident. Polished and sculpted, the marble proclaimed the existence of a higher order, an order in which man, by virtue of his nobility, became one with the divine, the only order that merits consideration, everything else being provisional, or a state of unworthy compromise.

This insurmountable distance was reflected here in the contrast between the mountain, where the marble workers lived in simple isolation, and the town, where everything, and especially the marble, was transfigured; between the poverty of the mountain people, their labours, and the wealth of the merchants below; between the coarse ugliness of the mountain women and the sleek beauty of those who walked along paved streets, often wearing marble buttons on their dresses, or malachite jewellery, ornaments of onyx or even ivory, mingled together, frivolous debris gathered in armfuls from the moraine which the marble thrust before it, in its endless descent, in the mist and in the sun . . .

. . . in the day, and sometimes, as night fell, in a last effort, with the pulleys screeching, as though in an attempt to complete some vague citadel as a defence against the oncoming darkness. At this hour, the rough-hewn marble, growing cold in the night air, was like any other stone, only vaster and more unmanageable, in the odour of the impatient horses.

One could hear the workers running to keep up with the whitish catafalque of the marble, along oak beams of the chute used to lower the blocks down the side of the mountain. Most of the men had wide torsos, rigid, overdeveloped chests, like large apes were it not for the thoughtful bearing of their heads, and their uplifted arms, which gesticulated silently – it was hard to say why – perhaps because of the speed with which they were running, or to maintain a balance on the wooden ties, flayed smooth, and shiny with grease.

In many parts of Italy, marble has been quarried by the same methods for centuries. The blocks of stone are slid down into the valley along wooden rails coated with grease. Running behind the marble, and holding the ropes which encircle it, the men regulate its speed and direction. All this would have been simple enough, in spite of the effort required, had there been only the slow, laborious 'lowering of the body' (the transport of the marble could easily be associated with a funeral ceremony). But at the entrance to the larger quarries there was a real traffic problem.

Tracks crossing, junctions where the wooden rails came loose beneath the weight and the wrenching motions of the blocks, parallel tracks, convoys passing one another, terraced landings where the men, suddenly released from the effort of braking their great burden, gave way to momentum, a complicated network of merging chutes, controlled landslides, all this chaos, regulated though it was, multiplied the danger.

Not so much the danger of being crushed beneath a block, of a flattened leg or a pulverized arm, but the danger, if a man wasn't watching, of being struck as the blocks slid by, in the back or the chest, rather like a nasty dig in the ribs in a rough dancehall, the beginning of a still unspoken quarrel, a blow which does not hurt until a few seconds later, when a weight gathers beneath the flesh as it turns black and blue, breath grows painfully short and the light keeps dimming in the silence of the pines and one feels upon one, perhaps as early as tomorrow, the marble touch of death.

This was why the men wound layers of cloth, felt, and leather around their chests, a soft armour which cushioned the impact of the marble. They defended themselves against the stone as they would against the cold, or, clad in cork life jackets which their bulky garb resembled, as they would against shipwreck.

By instinct, not because it afforded any sort of protection, they wore woollen caps pulled down over their eyes. Hooded and bundled up in this heavy clothing, they had a fierce, institutional look about them. Sometimes their austere, grotesque attire resembled the uniforms of jailkeepers buttoned to the neck and impervious to insult, at other times, it seemed like the mark of felony and servitude.

For up there on the mountain, power hung precariously in the balance. Near the summit, where the marble was quarried, it was hard to tell whether the men still dominated the stone, or whether they were already subject to the royalty which was latent in it and would emerge in the valley below. A royalty of many faces, only vaguely suggested by the variety of the marble.

Antique black, white, purple as in porphyry, dark grey veined in yellow as in portor, the same colour could suggest a funereal or a religious purpose just as well as profane ostentation. The same marble ensured the solemnity both of wealth and of death, thus affirming its steadfast loyalty to the order it served, proclaiming it loftily above the tombs. Preferably with the sound of foliage rustling endlessly in the wind.

For marble, even in its raw state, just out of the quarry, harmonizes with the most subtle effects of nature. Like stones submerged in a clear stream which revives their colouring, it accentuates the play of light and shadow and bears witness to the secret coolness that dwells behind the fevers of life, a permanent truth behind the clouds.

This truth penetrated the night, it penetrated the morning, the sunshine and the rain, from one end to another of the chain of mountains which ran down to the shore as far as the eye could see. All year long. The marble was excavated and its colour gave rise to vague speculations as to its purpose. It was lowered down into the valley as gently as possible. It passed through narrow corridors between the oak trees. It crossed clearings in the pine forests, or sloping wastelands overgrown with shrubs. There were days of gaiety, no one knew why; there were days of hatred, and always, in the background, the glacial serenity of truth.

Nothing ever changed, except the sea. It lay in the distance, blue, grey, or green, on windy days stippled with fleeting whitecaps, mercurial, a contrast to so much stability – marble of an inconstant variety.

Many of the workmen came from Romagna and were un-married. They were housed in barracks halfway up the moun-tainside, towards the eastern slope, on the side of the ravines. The sea was not visible from there. They rediscovered it every morning between two stretches of trees, as they climbed to the quarries. This daily encounter gave them a feeling not unlike the happy indolence of dawn which, in men at least, is accom-panied by desire.

Short of breath after the steep climb, they paused for a moment and stretched, looking at the sea. In the summer they dreamt of swimming but said nothing about it. The rest of the year, they said nothing, either, about what continued to haunt them at these moments. They would resume their climb, to-wards the marble, towards their unjust fate, their loneliness.

In the evening, when they fell asleep, desire did not visit their dreams. They dreamt only of crumbling stone, the clang of hammers and chisels. Of scaffolding, too, for their universe consisted in part of the vast construction built to support the chute along which the marble slid over hollows and valleys. Continually being strengthened, reinforced by the addition of new beams and girders, it was like an endless covered gangway, braced on all sides, a labyrinth of scaffolding in which the men moved about, made repairs, and took refuge from the rain, plucking pale weeds which grew among the stones, while the sea, far off, disappeared under a low grey sky.

One gang of men worked in a smaller quarry, where the marble was of the white variety known as statuary marble. It did not always have the purity demanded of it. The other kinds of marble sometimes turned out to be lumachel, a stone forma-tion that contains fossil shells and pulverized coral, but this was not important; there was a market for every sort. But the white marble, used by sculptors, could not contain a single fissure or blemish, still less any of the 'puffy' spots in which the chisel suddenly strikes a dull note as a bit of powdered debris falls away. The whole block was supposed to be 'proud', that is to say impenetrable, and white as lard.

They dug still further, hollowing vast galleries inside the quarry, as though, having dismissed the illusion of successive castles, they sought to excavate the very heart of the stone, to reach the black tabernacle hidden there. Even in the depths, purity was rare. Sometimes wormy striations ran through the blocks, rendered fragile by marine weevils five hundred thousand years before.

And when an immaculate lode had been found, and a block cut away as white and fine-grained as alabaster, even then, complete purity was not yet attained. In spite of its solidity, uniformity, there were still mysterious presences within the marble. It was destined, as they all knew, for the stonecutting industries in the largest town in the valley. They supplied half the country with pious statuary, mass-produced. A great variety of subjects was available to the clientele: baroque angels, saints in traditional attitudes, Virgins with Child, or Virgins alone. The Virgins were most in demand. Of all the statues, they were, no doubt, the most satisfying. The marble excavated from the small quarry, with its whiteness, its fine grain, its inner glow, could very properly be called *virginal*.

On holy days, when the workmen attended mass in town, or looked at the window displays of the marble dealers, they discovered this world of static beings which lay sleeping in the blocks they quarried on high. The sight of these figures, skilfully humanized by sculptors and then reproduced in quantity, made it possible, the rest of the week, to 'read into' the blocks of unhewn marble taken from the mountain. This was not so much imagination, for the workmen did little daydreaming, as it was the kind of mechanical reckoning in which people who are engaged in manual labour often indulge. Staring at the block of stone which they had just excavated, the men were led to trace in their minds the figure of this Virgin-to-be, and to lend her the necessary dimensions. The thickness of the block

seemed to determine them, and yet, allowing for the swelling
of the bosom here, and lower down, other feminine curves, a
vaguely sinuous outline took shape within the cold marble,
moving about, making the surface swell here and there, like a
serpent in a sack.

Their inability to place, or to replace, the Virgin in the block
of stone troubled the men, and not only professionally. It made
them feel ignorant as children. At one time or another they had
all seen naked women, had held them close while making love
and become familiar with their bodies. They now learned that
this familiarity was an illusion. Of all our memories, those of
love wear out most quickly; their presence lies to us. Soon they
are nothing more than an ephemeral web, a trace of ashes, a
foggy outline which, henceforth, only our irrational wills can
resurrect. Everything has fled, like water from between our
fingers, and we are faced, each time, with that virginity which
is perpetually reborn in desire.

It was the same with the sea, which they could make out
behind the oblique, stone-battered pines. In the rhythm of the
surf, out of the rippling water, the undulating currents, more
imprecise and at the same time more vital than the marble, a
distant but long-awaited presence might arise.

The workmen now knew that they would never find this long-
awaited presence – had they ever found it? – at the dances down
in the valley, where they took factory girls every weekend.
Sometimes the girls would offer themselves, in the grass in
summer, along the walls in winter, in the noise and smells of
the city, in laughter and confusion, fear and wantonness and a
concentrated sort of pleasure which made them dig their stubby
nails into the men's shoulders.

The next morning, the men climbed back up the face of the
quarry. The first shift was already setting off dynamite. The
smoke grew tattered in the pines, and echoes fled towards the
blue, green, grey sea, perpetually strewn with whitecaps and
dreams. A taste still in their mouths from the night before,
the men began once more to exhume the sarcophagi of

goddesses, hauling them up from the depths of the mountain. Accursed creatures, inaccessible and yet desired! They were dead, however, and knowing this, the men felt a certain sense of revenge. They laughed. Not at the Virgin – they did not dare – but at the saints. The thought of these cloddish peasants of the Faith, with their childish destiny, their absurd survival in the darkness of village churches, would sometimes fill the men with hate and scorn.

Even after they were sculpted, the saints would never escape the icy prison of the marble, a just fate which the men wished for their enemies, tyrannical foremen, faceless managers, or sometimes disloyal companions. Death should 'marbleize' them. For where there is hatred, death is not dead enough. It is a light sentence. It dissolves rather than imprisons. It blends us with the living world.

The men dreamt of a death heavy as marble, dragging its victims like drowned statues to the most obscure depths of the sea, abandoning them forever. And now, in their hearts, they wished that love could be as heavy, and they dreamt that somewhere in the world, in the darkness, a pure marble, pale and translucent as camphor, would open itself to receive them.

In the town where they went on Sundays, they happened to hear about a young woman who posed for one of the sculptors. He made models for the Virgins, but did not confine his skill to these. His income assured by pious subjects, he sculpted allegories which expressed, as he said, his true feelings and talent: Peace, the Seasons, the Spirit of the Waters – a multitude of naked virgins.

The young woman posed for each one of them, in turn. She had become the sculptor's mistress, having been the mistress of two of the principal marble merchants in town. She was beautiful, less full-blown than the other women of the region. Her body, not thin, *exact* one might say, gave an arresting sharpness, almost a perversity, to the symbols which took shape under the sculptor's chisel. The Virgins, too erect in their long robes, evoked that manner of self-assertion in sacrifice which makes love akin to despair. Peace suggested the still desire of women. The Seasons had deep eyes and a sad intensely questioning look on their faces. None of this was obvious, yet quietly, without shocking anyone, it replaced the traditional image of feminine patience and fertility with the poignant truth of love.

In the town, Clara was known to be fickle, not for motives of greed, but by nature. There was no trace of contempt in the reproach that surrounded her. When Clara passed through the streets of town, her elegance and pride left a wake of silence behind her. To comment, to question, might easily have led to the kind of conclusions after which life is nothing but disappointment and endurance.

It was thought unfortunate that Clara loved Manuce the sculptor, a paunchy man with wavy hair and a soft mouth beneath a thin black moustache. He was known to be avid for wealth and prizes. Did she really love him? Was it not just one of the thousand faces of her nakedness, one of the scattered images of herself reflected in the myriad statues, one of her functions as a public Virgin?

When they discovered that Clara existed, the marble workers were very bewildered. So the faceless woman whose fleeting dimensions they visualized within the marble was a creature of flesh and blood! They all wanted to see her, but Clara went out very rarely and besides, who would have pointed her out? She remained a distant image for them and her legend grew richer. Soon she came to embody Evil. The men thwarted their disappointment at not knowing Clara by relegating her to that alien, hostile world where women and marble are bought and sold. Clara was venal, corrupt. Her sins were not of the ordinary kind. Others had to be invented, still without names or shapes, maggots bred in the dregs of the night.

For with her, life was nothing but darkness. From now on, night would weigh heavily in the marble, not the clear night of the depths, but an indelible one, dark as the wine of depravity in the village inns. Why do women always pile one illusion upon another? Because of women, the men thought, in the end they might not even be able to look at the sea without suffering.

Among the workers in the quarry of white marble, all mature men, aware of the sadness of their life but knowing that it was too late to start out on another, was a boy of barely twenty, named Carlo. After floods had ruined his family's farm, somewhere near the Po, he had come to work on the mountain, while waiting to find something better. His face had a gentle, childlike quality, in contrast to the vigour of his body, developed by the heavy work with the marble. Docile, not talkative, embarrassed by his overly virile build, he aroused paternal feelings in the other workers. They admired him for being so obliging and courageous in this inferior sort of work, into which he had been forced by an unjust fate.

This high regard was shared by the foremen, who often entrusted Carlo with the most desirable tasks, without any bitterness on the part of the others. This was the reason why Carlo was chosen, one day, to go along on the truck which was taking a block of marble to Manuce. The sculptor had received an unexpected commission and was short of material. Carlo was to help the driver unload the stone.

They had arrived in the courtyard of the house where Manuce lived and were sliding the stone off the platform of the truck when the driver lost his grip and a corner of the stone struck Carlo in the chest. Before coming to town, he had taken off the chest padding which the men wore in the quarry. It was hot. His shirt was open. The sharp corner of the marble gashed his chest which began to bleed.

Manuce, who was watching as they unloaded the stone, became concerned and took Carlo into his house. The boy was mopping up the blood with his handkerchief and kept repeating that it was only a scratch. But Manuce had a compassionate soul; his art made it necessary. Besides, he found Carlo endearing. He saw him as Saint Sebastian. He brought the boy into the hall which led to the studio and called Clara through the door.

Carlo had often heard about Clara at the quarry. He was stricken with shyness. He said that the wound was nothing: it had stopped bleeding. He lifted the handkerchief which he held against his chest; the wound was still bleeding. The door opened. Clara was drawing her dressing gown about her.

'Make a bandage for him,' Manuce said to her. 'I'll help the driver bring in the stone.'

Clara asked Carlo to follow her. They walked across the studio. The light had a wintry harshness. Carlo noticed that Clara's hair was very black. It was tied back and fell over one shoulder, baring the curved, lightly-tanned nape of her neck. Clara went up the stairs leading to two rooms arranged along a gallery. She stopped for a moment, lifted one foot and turned halfway around to take off the sandal, in which one of the chips of marble strewn around the studio must have caught. While shaking it, she moved her toes. Carlo looked at the bare foot. His heart began to pound. He looked up. His eyes met those of Clara as she put her sandal back on.

They entered a small dressing room. Carlo leaned back against the frame of the door and lifted his handkerchief from his chest. The wound was no longer bleeding. He waited, holding his shirt open. He felt ridiculous. Clara bent over a small cabinet looking for medicines. The top of her dressing gown hung open. Carlo saw her breasts. He heard his heart beating. When she applied the bandage to the wound, which was on his left side, Clara would feel the hammering beneath her fingertips.

She stood up, looked into Carlo's eyes, and closed her dressing gown. She came closer, wiped the wound with a piece of cotton wool dipped in alcohol, and applied a compress. She held it there, with the palm of her hand. Carlo's heart was still beating very fast. After the icy burn of the alcohol, he felt the weight and the warmth of Clara's hand through the gauze.

Beyond the compress, her fingers and painted nails exerted

a gentle, irregular pressure against his bare chest, as though the vibration of his heart beneath her palm carried into her fingertips. Once again their eyes met. Clara's expression was stern. Carlo's burned. He was the first to lower his eyes.

Manuce and the driver came into the studio, pushing the marble on a low cart. Manuce was talking loudly and laughing. He liked to show that physical effort exhilarated him. He often would imagine his sculpture as a gentle but herculean labour.

Carlo, leaning in the doorway which opened on to the balcony, could be seen from the back of the studio. Moving slightly to one side, Clara drew him further into the room. As she did so, he felt a desire to lay his hand on her hair. He would not have been able to say why he started to do this. Clara seized his wrist and laid his hand over her own. Then she took hers away. He understood that he was to hold the compress while she found a bandage. She applied two pieces of adhesive to hold the dressing on his chest.

Then, as if she wanted to show that the treatment was over, or as if she wanted a last remembrance of his contact they had shared, she laid her right hand in the middle of Carlo's gleaming chest, slowly spread her fingers, lifted them, smiled, and suddenly turning away, went to replace the gauze and medicine in the cabinet. Carlo stammered a word of thanks and went out quickly, buttoning his shirt.

During the whole trip back, he could not escape a feeling of oppression. He was quickly winded as he climbed back to the quarry, along the tracks where the men, tugging at ropes around the stone, shouted words he did not understand. He had to stop on the way to catch his breath. It was at one of the places which had a view of the sea, but Carlo did not notice.

That night, in bed, he ripped the bandage off his chest. He lay down on the wound. It smarted slightly. He was thinking of Clara. He could see the heavy twist of wavy black hair falling over her right shoulder, her breasts with the nipples gleaming in the shadow of the dressing gown, her deep, sad eyes. The next day, his feelings still in a tumult, he went back to the quarry.

Unlike his fellow workers, he had never imagined presences within the marble. The murky discussions of his elders alluding to saints and virgins inside the stone had appeared to him as a kind of necessary irreverence, justified by a hard and lonely life. When they ran their large hands like calipers over the surface of the marble, pretending to take Clara's measurements, making various comments which contrasted the chill of the stone with certain nameless fires, Carlo would walk away, embarrassed by this spectacle of mental onanism.

Now, everything had changed. The jokes of the others about the future statues of the Virgin Clara were painful to him. Even more painful were the daydreams of his own imagination. And yet it was true that from the blocks of marble rose visions of the one who had caressed his chest, who belonged to him even more than if she had given herself, for such furtive gestures, such a suggestive complicity of the flesh, was the body's equivalent of whispering, which always conveys more feeling than a direct statement. And yet it was true that, aside from the moments when she represented the Holy Virgin, Clara posed in the nude for a man who was her lover.

A never-ending reminder. Even though every one of the blocks of stone cut from the quarry could not be destined for Manuce and those who made copies of his work, there was always one, among those being lowered down the mountain, which carried Clara within it like a corpse, which took her away from him forever and delivered her into the hell of nakedness.

Summer had come. The sun warmed the marble, gave it a blinding whiteness. From the shade of the pines, the blocks of stone could be seen passing along the open track, radiant with glory. Beyond lay the sea, also brilliant. Distant joys. On the mountain, summer was parched, it lit up the landslides and the cliffs of broken marble, in the shade of which rose only the aromatic bitterness of the gorse.

One Sunday, Carlo went down to town and hid himself beyond a porte-cochère opposite Manuce's house. He remained there several hours. Towards evening, Clara and Manuce drove out of the courtyard. Carlo took one step from behind the porte-cochère. While Manuce was busy manœuvring the car, Clara saw him. She gave him an intense look. The car drove away.

The following evening, Carlo returned to town, having asked the foreman, under false pretences, to leave work earlier than usual. He took up his post again. A quarter of an hour later, Clara crossed the street and entered the porte-cochère. Since the evening before, she had been watching for Carlo. She did not hold out her hand, and said very little. She kept turning around to look into the street. They arranged to meet the following Sunday in a little village outside of town. She was very prompt for their rendezvous. They walked out into the countryside and became lovers.

From then on, they met two or three times a week at a little inn on the outskirts of town. When the weight of silence had lifted slightly between them, when they were somewhat more free from the oppression of love, they began to talk about their lives. Carlo ordered Clara to leave Manuce. She asked for more time. Carlo lost his temper. Then they made love again, as though closing their eyes against too bright a light.

After a while, it happened that some of the men from the quarry saw Carlo and Clara together, as the two were leaving the inn. Clara's elegant beauty made them take notice. They questioned the innkeeper who knew everyone in town, and learned that Carlo's mistress was Clara of the statues.

The news spread over the mountain. Carlo's fellow workers were shocked. The fatherly emotions they felt towards him were hurt. They would have been delighted if good luck had come his way and he had accepted it with the cynicism which, to them, was inseparable from virility. But to love Clara was to become a part of the sacrilege which she committed by giving herself to men, hardly yet out of the marble, her body still rigid from posing as the Virgin of Saint-Sulpice. Even more exposed to the kisses of others than the statue of Saint-Appollinea of Manteleco, she was dragging Carlo into degradation. Didn't he realize this?

Carlo lowered his head. He did not know how to answer the older men. He did not want to give up Clara. He thought that she should live with him, should leave Manuce and stop acting as a model. He told her this. Once again she smiled at his impetuosity. She was afraid of poverty and was not sure she would always love Carlo.

Meanwhile, at the quarry, reproach had given way to insults. Carlo was surrounded by contempt. He began to be ashamed of himself. He kept out of sight as he walked down the mountain, taking different paths from the others, climbing down through the landslides, sometimes falling. He would linger there for a moment, his hands among the stones, stunned, out of breath, hesitating before rising again, hoping to wake up later in the calm clarity of the night. But soon he would set off and arrive at the inn. Clara would be waiting for him, sitting in a corner of the darkened room. She would undress, they would make love, and when night fell, Carlo would climb back along the jagged path of the landslide, alone again, among the stones.

After this torment had lasted a few weeks, Carlo resolved never to see Clara again. He told his fellow workers. They congratulated him.

He found he could not sleep any more. In the evening, he went to watch the sea between the pines. When the weather was clear, he was able to make out the pattern of the currents, and the oscillating streak of the waves. The glow of the sand, still visible in the darkness, followed the indented outline of the coast.

Why did life have so many faces, and which one of them was the face of goodness and truth? Was the sea, with all it offered; drowned hair streaming, the hipline of the breakers, the murmuring of the deep, the insidious burn of the salt, fleeting currents, lukewarm or cold, a reprieve from death, the rhythmic abandon of swimming found nowhere else but in love, yes, all this, was it not merely one realm to be chosen among many, as real as the others, no more, no less, surrounded by *terra firma*, with mysterious outlines, channel zones, and lagoons?

Strange world of adjacent truths, in which the marble and the sea could have fulfilled one another, but instead were divided, where a chasm separated on the one side the slow, sightless roaming of the algae, the restive motion of the tides, the opaque lights, and on the other, the marble castles, stripped bare by avalanches, shining, cold, sharpening their bladelike edges in the wind, lofty symbols of good, cathedrals of perfection, high over the suffering pines, the hypocritical shade of the bushes, the men swathed in felt and bound to blocks of stone which they lowered endlessly towards the valley, along the creaking oaken tracks.

Clara was hurt by Carlo's absence, and even more by his scorn. She, too, felt that her trouble was like the sea. Everything which she had known, suffered, survived, everything she had loved, rejoiced in before her love for Carlo now seemed like nothing more than a parade of dead statues, wan effigies. She was chilled by all the marble to which she had lent her presence, in the hope that by multiplying images of herself she might eventually be able to believe in life.

She suffered in these dazzling summer days, when, along the deserted streets, trucks would sometimes pass, carrying blocks of unhewn marble straight from the quarries, marked with a red cross and a number which she had never noticed until then, haunting reminders, in all this sunshine, of the infamy of tombs and statues. And she could not stop seeing before her eyes the awkward, strange boy who, one already distant morning, had arrived before her with blood on his chest, that mute boy, bitten by the marble, whose eyelids fluttered, the boy who made her want to bite him. Why didn't he come back? But she knew why. She decided to leave Manuce. First she would go up to the quarry and tell Carlo.

She drove along a road which led to the slope opposite the

one used to lower the marble. She parked her car at the foot and started up a path towards the summit. It soon disappeared into a heap of fallen rock. Along the edge of the ravine left by the landslide, grew stunted oaks and bushes whose parched and whitened roots hung out into space.

Clara continued her ascent over the rocks. Further on, she had to penetrate a thicket which barred the way. Thorns caught in her dress and scratched her legs and hands. Clouds of pollen and insects rose around her in the heat trapped by the dense shrubbery. Clara grew weary. Sweat made her hair cling to her brow. She felt a painful, bitter thirst, no doubt because of the acrid dust rising from the bushes. She was angry at herself for having worn a black dress – an absurd choice, simply because it suited her dark looks. The sun, beating down on the heavy linen, made her back burn. Would she ever reach the top?

She was surprised not to hear any noise from the quarries, situated just over the crest. She climbed more and more slowly, twisting her ankle now and then on the rocks which loomed up one by one, as did the scars in the ground, the furrows left by the rain, the dents in the earth where pebbles nested, round or oblong, with yellow and white markings. Frightened, out of breath, she stopped for a moment, in a kind of stupor. What was she doing there, halfway up this scorched and lonely mountain, she who lived in cool houses, nude and idle?

Below her, the valley already lay blue in the distance, with its miniature villages, its checkerboard of fields and network of roads and streams. Clara was amazed to have climbed so high already, and felt an extraordinary joy coming over her. She looked at the sun-whitened sky and rejoiced in the burning heat, the solitude. She rejoiced in her suffering and her thirst, and continued once more on her way to the top.

She was almost there when she heard a horn sounding twice. She did not know what it meant but, thinking the sounds came from the quarry, she set out in the direction from which she had heard them, slightly to her right, on the other side of a cliff projecting from the ridge. The horn again sounded twice.

Drawn on by the joy of having reached the end of her climb, and still full of the exhilaration which had come over her on the way, Clara climbed faster.

She finally emerged on the slope where the quarries lay, beneath overhanging precipices, studded with enormous sections of marble, intersected with wooden chutes leading down into the valley. She climbed down to the foot of the cliff. The blocks of marble formed a shadowy corridor. She heard someone call.

Quite far below her, a curiously dressed man, his woollen hat pulled down over his eyes, was gesturing wildly in her direction. She could not understand what he was shouting. He began to run, still shouting, towards a place on the flank of the mountain which was hidden from Clara by the blocks of marble. She was leaning back with great joy, feeling the chill of the stone invade her body. Behind the marble, the man was still shouting.

The dynamite went off. The front of the cliff detached itself slowly, split open in all directions, hung motionless for a second in the suddenly silent, fire-blue air, and collapsed over Clara in a cloud of marble dust.

Since the laying of the explosives meant a brief rest for the workmen, Carlo had walked into the pine forest. He was looking at the sea. He was saying to himself that, after all, the sea could also be an image of goodness and truth. He resolved to go back to Clara that night, in town.

translated by Merloyd Lawrence

The Forest Fire

From the window of her hotel bedroom Rose, that year, could see the sea. This was a sort of promotion, the exact degree of which could have been gauged from the list of charges in force at that seaside resort: Rose could still see only a tiny bit of sea.

It lay between two houses and under the armpit of a great tree, whose main branches grew rather low. The sea horizon disappeared among the leaves, nesting somewhere, perhaps beside that half-seen bird stirring up there, preening its feathers and those of the distant water and the vanishing sails. . . .

The presence of such trees, with their flat leaves, downy or speckled (she did not know their names; unlike the pines which merged in a uniform rustle of needles – a dry prickly sea whose colour rippled like the other sea's – these trees spread out in an infinite network of veins like a diagram of the human body), the presence of these big debonair trees so near the sea had always disturbed her. She had the same feeling about certain animals.

The sight of a horse thrusting its nostrils close to a wave gave her an impression of incompatibility so cruel that she felt almost sick. This was a shaggy, stocky horse, inclined to droop its head; and that day, as on almost every day, there was a wind blowing, a clear sky, a bright sun. The sight of that tree, and of that horse (it belonged to a man shovelling sand) made Rose painfully aware of the cruel saltness cleaving the world in two, teasing man's thirst, setting a barrier of foam between earth with its garment of seasons and that limitless, opaque universe.

Rose's feet, still shod, crushed a narrow ridge of seashell fragments, the screenings of the abyss, in which the water of the dying wave went on crackling faintly like an acid, as far as the ear could hear, as far as the shore could reach.

From her window, however, she could see nothing, for the time being, but that tree stranded on the edge of the sea, full of a bitter sap, and shaking in the lonely wind its foliage in which the sea shimmered white, nest-high.

A fortnight before, a doctor had told her to try the sea. It was the advice of a man who feels himself hemmed in: he had recommended space. He might perhaps not have spoken so definitely had not his eye lighted, through his study window, on a providential patch of blue that looked, just then, as if it overhung a sea horizon. Below, in the hot July sunshine, lay Paris beneath a storm cloud of petrol fumes. The doctor had spoken out of his deepest need.

He had prescribed the Atlantic, no less.

A few days later Rose packed a couple of suitcases with some linen garments, bought hurriedly and scored with creases, and the barely begun manuscript of her translation of *A Lamp at Noon* by the English writer John Abberton-Lorris, who was still unknown in France.

'It's up to you that he should cease to be so,' she had been told, kindly but firmly, by the Paris publisher for whom she worked.

He was a man of about sixty, with thinning hair, white at the temples. He was slight, beardless, dressed in grey, easy to describe and inviting similes.

'I shan't budge this year myself,' he had told Rose, laying his hand on the pile of papers that lay beside him. 'Just a day or two around August 15th, and the odd weekend. . . .'

He spoke without a trace of discontent or resentment, but with obvious satisfaction. In his usual easygoing way he included himself among those who, that summer, had decided 'not to budge' and who, before returning to their reports and figures, waved a cheerful, indulgent goodbye to those who were preparing to go off. A deep complicity united such men; they had drawn time itself into their league; that summer had become a bourgeois summer. Others, staying or going, would be copying their attitudes. Rose was going. The prices she might pay at the seaside had nothing to do with the matter.

'Oh, one day we shall all be burnt,' she had said to the publisher to show him that, in spite of everything, she was not taken in.

'D'you think so?' he had asked with a smile, for he was used to dealing sympathetically with the intellectuals he employed. Their unexpected phrases, their anguish! He would listen to them, particularly those that had official titles, and afterwards, waiting in his bed for sleep to come, he would sometimes worry about the approach of death. Then day would dawn again.

'Do you think so?' he had repeated. 'If you mean the atomic war, well, after all, that's not quite true. To begin with, the war's not here yet, thank Heaven, and even if it were there'd still be a chance for a few of us. . . . If it's Hell you mean, we've been in the dark about that since the beginning of time, unless you're better informed than I am. Look, since we're talking of Hell (and what a foolish thing to do in weather like this!), since we're talking of Hell, I'd like to draw your attention to a book we're bringing out in a day or two. It's most curious – an aesthetic explanation of Hell. We all know Art has a diabolic basis but Brunier, the author – he's a professor – develops the theme in a highly original way. I'll send it to you. . . . Meanwhile, talking of burns, do take precautions against sunburn on your beach. And don't forget me! I want your manuscript by the end of August. Is that agreed?'

The sea lay in the tree, under the tree, like a cloth spread for an abandoned picnic, bitter, desolate. . . . The wind always got up a little in the late afternoon, and the sea grew darker. Then the tree, with all its leaves blown upward by the wind, seemed more emphatically upright than before, as though taken aback, almost rearing before the oncoming infinity of water.

Rose had turned into the avenue overlooking the beach in the late afternoon. The engine, red hot after the long journey, was knocking, and there was a smell of hot leaking oil. Below, the sand was strewn with bodies. The only creatures moving were small children bent over their spades, suddenly quarrelling, looking like miniature gravediggers, overworked and angrily despairing of ever coping with so many recumbent figures.

Occasionally somebody would get up, take a few steps, wiping the sand off the back of his thighs, then start to run towards the long low wave, his feet seeming winged with water as they struck it. A few seconds later he had disappeared, he had become one of the crowd of decapitated heads borne on the surface of the water (and a gleam of silver slid over the darkened sea), heads floating aimlessly, with the set smile that accompanies a feat of strength, so that each swimmer looked like the top acrobat of a human pyramid, smiling on behalf of the rest, in this case to avert the insidious collapse of the water.

A few men and women, having dressed again, were already leaving the beach. Only their children, still practically naked, went on squabbling over a handful of seaweed. Rose marvelled at the calm displayed by those who for no apparent reason were the first to leave the sand. Perhaps they had all they wanted? They had expected nothing and nothing had come. They went back to their hired huts, brick blocks of varying sizes, mostly hidden behind tamarisk hedges. Some women were talking loudly amidst a smell of open-air cooking. The man wore a short-sleeved cotton shirt the colour of burnt bread, grey linen trousers and, on his feet, crepe-soled sandals with leather straps.

'I've told you a hundred times not to bring seaweed into the garden!'

Bathing suits were drying on a line. The wind was blowing again; the woman put her hand to her hair; things were falling from the trees.

Rose had at last reached the hotel where she had reserved a room by telephone, two days before, after consulting a list. It was called the Hotel Stella. It stood at some distance from the town, in the middle of a largish garden where borders of shells marked off the shrubberies. There was a big main building of farmhouse type with a dovecote at one end. In order to preserve its rustic character – belied, however, by the name of the hotel, relic of a fashion already a quarter of a century old – the supporting beams of the façade had been left exposed and painted 'wood colour'.

Rose had been surprised to find her room so small and set back from what was called here 'the sea front'. Her complaint was met with a bored reminder of the list of charges; she had chosen the lowest and she ought to be pleased! It was not entirely devoid of a sea view . . . Then Rose had gone to open the french window and had seen the tree.

It stood between two rather mean-looking houses, solitary and almost outcast, shading the sort of things that are commonly found in the yards of outhouses: an old grindstone, a broken garden table, a rusty remnant of agricultural machinery – an iron stem ending in a toothed wheel, which an elderly man, to judge by his dress something between a workman and a concierge, would come and hold in his hands and examine at great length, with that air of furtive idleness which, on a rainy afternoon, makes aimless puttering seem fraught with sinister intentions; he would lay it down again just as the rain began to rustle in the leaves once more (on the slate roofs, close by, it only sounded intermittently, like running sand).

She stood at her open window while, behind her, the

chambermaid bustled about – one of those thin, grey-faced girls of about thirty who rush through the hotel season as if it were a marathon race, ceaselessly pushing back from their foreheads, with a gesture of weary irritation, a lank lock of dark hair. Rose lingered there, brooding over the evident kinship that bound her to that tree standing there, forgotten and exposed to the threatening sea.

She ought never to have chosen this hotel; it was a mistake that exposed her to the most blatant degradation. Distance alone can sometimes make inequality bearable, but when the distance is only that between two bends in a corridor or between two floors, inequality becomes an open wound, everything reverberates ominously: footsteps growing distant, voices answering each other, saying things you can't understand, a child's cry, the rain in a tree, all form part of that network of sounds in which the lonely heart lives through its pain again, as though watching a blurred, too-familiar film which always skips in the same places.

No, she should never have chosen this hotel. She could see herself in her corner of the façade while, at the further end, within the the dovecote itself, there were luxurious rooms with lace doilies on the tables – not, as here, just one stuck down under the glass plate of the single small table. She could watch herself being impelled towards the window, simultaneously with all the other guests, some night for instance, by an unaccustomed sight – preferably one that lit up the scene, a fire on the beach or out at sea.

And then the façade would begin to look like a page stuck all over with windows, a sheet of transfers illustrating social life, covered with animated engravings, like stamps, showing couples standing as though in theatre boxes; the woman would disappear inside the room among the flickering shadows to fetch a shawl or a sweater, and on her return the man would point out to her the tail end of some incident that she had missed and the place where it had happened; the spectators, from time to time, would talk to each other from their respective windows and a man with greying hair, from an upper story, would let fall some witticism; he would be the first to laugh at it and the others would lean back to look up at him, smiling, the women displaying their bosoms; a little way in front of the porch, on the steps of which the members of the reception staff stood smoking cigarettes, the manager of the hotel, a man dressed like a summer visitor but fatter than the rest, would gaze out at the beach and reply without turning round to the questions – some serious, some ironic – that were put to him.

Rose was all alone at the far end, the dark end of the façade; she was lost in the shadow of the trees, hidden among the buttresses; she pictured herself as smaller than the rest – her window was the smallest – looking like a sleepy servant girl in a cotton wrap, seeing almost nothing of the sight and yet laughing with the others who, oblivious of her presence, were like fleshy flowers that had the power of speech; while she had come to the edge of things, the place where your finger gliding over a surface reaches the rim and finds nothing beyond. . . .

The doctor must have been wrong. He had recommended the ozone. 'We've got to take a few risks. Granted, your nerves are over-wrought; but I think the primary cause of your nervous state lies in your anemia, in the impoverished condition of your blood. . . .'

Rose had hurried towards that ozone; the last few days in Paris her lips had constantly formed the word, as though she were learning a lesson by heart. She had reached the crowded beach and had stood in the background, by that lonely tree, without experiencing anything but those gusts of wind and the feeling of her own exclusion.

She questioned her sense of smell, her windpipe, her lungs, she would willingly have questioned her blood; perhaps they concealed some experience? Perhaps they were being imbued with an unfamiliar truth, while she listened to the tree and the rain and mentally opened the hotel's thousand windows on to the nocturnal spectacle, which all the others were watching, like a brilliant line of pictures from which her own little window was being removed, like a rejected canvas. Was this ozone? Was this the sea? She felt that she would be driven to that act beyond which there is no hope of redress, no possibility of living: the act of denouncing things themselves, of denouncing the false face of wood, the deceitfulness of steel, the cry in the earth, the mockery in a flower. Her first night had been sleepless and exhausting. Then she had decided to force herself to spend her time like the other guests in the hotel.

So she had resorted, of her own free will, to the therapy of submissiveness, hoping that ozone and the rest of it would come to her aid. In the intervals of bathing, resting, taking refreshment on the terrace of the Florida café, she went for walks in the pinewoods, over a mixture of needles and sand. A path led down through brambles to a sunny creek.

One morning she was sitting on a rock around which the wave was busily creeping with a slight hiss, which seemed, in that utter stillness, to be made less by the turning tide than by the sucking sand. The wind had not yet risen. Suddenly she had felt a pervading sense of exaltation and peace, that early-morning happiness which, by noon or even before, gives place to a torrid calm, an excitement already secretly weighed down by despair.

Her eyes closed, she was back at Viareggio, where she had been last summer. They had come down from Siena, where in the gloomy Guelph streets they had tried to conjure up the days of the 'wolves' (those fur-clad Italians, white-faced with hatred, seen in old pictures) and instead had all at once conjured up the days of the plague, that fetid exhalation rising from the depths of a medieval house, that warm tawny vapour that overhung the town, particularly around the unfinished new Cathedral, like a huge Leonardesque sketch (in the black and white of the old one, by its side, the very hues of terror seemed to have been constricted into an architectural corset from which they would only escape at nightfall). And meanwhile, in spite

3*

of that yellow, scorching, maybe malignant atmosphere, a school of music was practising Vivaldi above some arcade. From the top of the Del Mangia tower the town, with its coiled streets, its roofs of bright clay glittering in the sun, looked like a sleeping snake, splendid and pestilential. . . .

The snake, the very emblem of discord. Why had he said that? After all, it was he who'd begun it. . . . As they made their way down to the coast, leaving Siena behind them under its canopy of storm cloud, their quarrel had quickly grown, its original cause forgotten like some tiny, dark pestilence-breathing vent-hole; the town had encircled it, closed in upon it, and at last a hill had hidden it all from view.

In the evening light, amidst the Tuscan countryside, Rose had discovered that she did not really love this man. They had decided a few months earlier, to live together as often as they could. They had not often been able to do so. Their holidays together, their journey had been in the nature of a test. When they reached Viareggio, they parted company. He was a man of about thirty, simple and straightforward. It was quite likely that he suffered a great deal.

Next morning Rose had walked through a pinewood and gone to sit, just as she was doing today, beside the waves. What did it all mean? Whether we let our lives be guided by the heart or by the reason, we are likely to make a mess of things in the end. The most commonplace misunderstanding, the simplest disagreement, the sense of having dealt an unfair wound, are enough to prove the blue sky black, and for the rest of our lives the light of the world will flicker ominously. . . .

Dazed by the sunshine and by her memories. Rose was walking back to the Hotel Stella along the coast, when she caught sight of some smoke rising above the pine trees, some way behind her. It was still visible from the hotel gardens, and the guests who had already assembled for their meal had left the dining room to watch the progress of the fire. Some of them thought it must be on the outskirts of the airfield, others shook their heads with smiling disbelief:

'I passed that way in the car, coming back from tennis, less than an hour ago. I didn't see anything.'

'But my dear fellow, you couldn't have seen anything. The trees would have hidden the flames from you, even if they were less than a hundred yards from the road, and look, the wind was driving the smoke not in your direction but towards the sea. . . .'

'If the fire goes on spreading this way, the golf course will soon cut it off,' somebody pointed out in a deep voice.

The fire itself was hemmed in by their familiar landmarks: the airfield where the more experienced and the more daring of them hired biplanes that flew low over the hotel, with an alarming noise like aerial motorcycles and a rocking motion of their wings; the tennis courts over the red earth of which they sent their balls skidding, and then took up their positions again in tight-lipped silence; the golf course over whose ups and downs they walked without hurrying and without speaking, like people making their way to look at a plot of land for sale; the paths through the pinewoods, too, where they went trotting on their hired hacks, unalterably solemn, stiffly and proudly poised and staring straight ahead, and finally the road along which, between Le Fiquet and Nource, one of them was just claiming to have taken his car at over eighty miles an hour.

'Oh, Charles, you never told me that! No, don't protest, you took good care not to tell me!' exclaimed, in a tone of radiant indignation that betrayed her pride, a dark young woman with an affected, rather languid voice.

The men laughed. One of them protested with a marked shade of gallantry: 'Speed is a virile fault, Madame. . . .'

She shook her head, appealing to another woman near her to witness: 'Listen to them!'

But the other had turned towards the façade of the hotel: 'Mademoiselle!' she sang out. 'Mademoiselle!' she repeated in the same singsong tone, addressing an open window of the dovecote. 'I want to make sure from the nurse that the children's tray has been taken up. The whole staff seems to have gone crazy because of this fire,' she exclaimed to those around her.

'Well, suppose we go in to lunch all the same?' The man looked at the watch on his hairy wrist.

'Oh, I've just seen a flame!' cried one of the women who had moved away to find a better viewpoint and had just clambered on to a garden chair.

Now she must have felt the men's gaze on her legs like another fire, a familiar one this time, smouldering quietly, its glow rising to her thighs so that she felt like a lamp gently shining under the pink shade of her dress. 'I can't see any more . . .' she said in a solemn girlish voice and, bending down, she prepared to jump off the chair, holding down her skirt over her knees with both hands.

'No, it's a State forest,' declared one of the men severely. 'That's why it's so badly kept up. They don't do enough clearing. . . .'

'I'm going to give up riding there, that's all; the briers close off half the paths.'

'Are you coming, Charles, I'm dying of hunger,' cried the dark young woman, also in a singsong, as she reached the porch.

The men made their way towards her, still chatting. They stopped once more in front of a big car that belonged to one of them, and pensively examined its tyres.

'I thought you'd seen this one of mine before. . . .'

The young woman in the pink dress was tucking her chin into her neck to look at her necklace, at which her companion, standing before her, was pointing with her little finger, commenting on its originality no doubt, or its brilliance: 'Just like your eyes.' The men walked heavily up the porch steps, three solid figures abreast. They were about to sweep along in their calm impetus the two young women who, close together, were looking down and talking to the green necklace. No, they had stopped. There were more laughing exclamations. Three other people had just come out of the hall, two more young women, suntanned and proud. The third, a man, laid his arm round the shoulders of one of the first group: 'Well, Charlie? . . .' They were talking about the fire again. They were looking back at the garden in the middle of which Rose was left standing alone, in the broad sunlight. They had not seen her. They would never see her.

Rose began to realize, with some disquiet, how much is lost during the passage into reality from dream. Her vision, which as she now discovered had been akin to premonition, had set the fire blazing by night. All the windows of the hotel had opened at once, with people in every room. The allotting of honours, privileges, secret partnerships to some, and to her, out on the left, of bitter solitude, bondage and betrayal, had all taken place on one plane. In that façade ablaze with reflected flames Rose had merely been 'the one who does not get saved'; the others were talking to the firemen, whose ears were deaf to her. Everything is simple, when it's liable to kill you.

But now the event, escaping from the truth of dreams, was passing into fact. Pine trees were burning. The smoke from the forest fire rose at first straight up into the sky in a column that bent slightly towards the sea and then spread out against an invisible ceiling, some air current, some harder vein running through the azure, some transparent obstacle against which the whole forest fire, its smoke, its glow opened out into an enduring cloud. Reality had established its distances. Here they were repeated, though on a diminished scale. Rose was in the middle of the garden, the others stood near the top of the porch steps, and the fire was going on in the far distance, out on the right. Thus through all our conflicts there is a free flow of air; misfortune is constantly being dispersed, despair itself is an elusive treasure; the echo of a vaster air intrudes unceasingly into our sobs, and life itself continues to breathe through our grief; except for death, nothing is given us in a state of purity.

Rose stood motionless, under the bright sunlight, in the middle of the garden. The people on the steps (had they stopped talking? their voices could no longer be heard) were

identical with those who are summoned betimes to be present
at some court murder or some ceremony of law-giving at
which solemn vows will be taken in silence, with raised hands,
who stand leaning against a pillar or in some window recess,
ready to emerge from their seeming aloofness and neutrality at
an appointed signal; they wait there as though bewitched, their
feet motionless as though nailed to the tiled floor that spreads
out in a pattern of great black and white diamonds. It all seems
so natural; one cannot utter a cry yet!

'Can't you find your table, Mademoiselle?'

The dining room which Rose had now entered was a huge
room panelled with dark wood. Blinds protected it from the
sun. Coming in out of the broad daylight, Rose found herself
blinded in this half-darkness through which waiters in white
jackets were scurrying. One of them led her to her table, and
she sat down. Another, holding a plate, bent over her. His
brow was beaded with plebeian sweat. One of his fellows was
leaning against a sideboard, his hands behind his back, in a
ritual attitude to which his half-smile, deliberately directed over
the heads of the guests in an effort to appear enigmatic, gave
an air of crafty expectation. He seemed to encourage, with
his smile, the cruel comings and goings of his companions
who, with dizzy speed, flashed through the dining room in
their white liveries, stained between the shoulders with a patch
of sweat like the print of a wet hand.

Muffled, brief words escaped them and they flew towards you
even faster, their eyes slightly averted from the steaming dishes
they held out to you. A conspiratorial hubbub rose from the
whole room. Rose could eat nothing: she kept sending the
dishes away, one after the other.

She had never felt so wretched. Seas were in league against
her. There was one, beyond the blinds – she could guess at it –
that went on breaking in tepid surf, tirelessly unfolding its
waves over the sand as though reiterating endless proofs –
although you were utterly convinced already – of the truth of
salt, water and space; and the other, the expanse of other

people, speaking with a voice like the sea's, self-contained, with the profound and total coherence of water, a dark smooth force, rearing its crested waves and scattering its foam. . . . Black pebbles? But we have black pebbles! Strange weeds, queer fish? We have them too! A broken shell, no, not as simple as that, a shell with a bevelled edge, a scaly shell with a mother-of-pearl bloom, they had one too. . . . 'They haven't got me! I don't belong to their world, to their camp, to their class, to their party.' Rose could have cried. 'I don't belong to their bourgeoisie!'

'Would you allow me to open this window a tiny bit?' asked a man sitting at the next table. He had got up. Rose was sitting next to the window; she raised her hand towards the bolt. The man hurriedly forestalled her: 'Oh, please, allow me, don't put yourself out.' Delicately he pushed it open. 'Not too much air for you?'

Rose shook her head.

'The fact is,' said the man, sitting down again in front of his companion, a woman with bare shoulders who kept running the back of her hand under her fringe of blonde hair, 'it's stifling outside too. It must be the forest fire warming us up,' he added with a laugh.

'Nothing to joke about, my dear chap,' cried another guest sitting behind Rose. 'It appears to be quite a serious matter. All the fire brigades of the region have been sent for. The local one must be on its way already. . . .'

'It won't get beyond Le Fiquet; they say the fire has reached the road already.'

'But there's a path along the coast, it's still clear,' said Rose. 'That's the way I came back a short while ago.'

'Good Lord, were you in the forest when the fire began?' said a young woman in a white dress looking at Rose with a sort of disgust. 'You might have been surrounded by the flames!'

'No, the fire started just as I was leaving the forest,' Rose answered.

At that moment, some words spoken at the next table reached their ears. 'No, you can't deny the existence of a certain popular vandalism. I'd be prepared to swear that this fire is the result of a criminal attempt, or the culpable negligence of campers or ramblers. . . . Oh, I know—' and the man raised his white hand in the gloom, 'when it's a question of responsibility . . .'

'And we were hoping to play golf later in the afternoon,' the young woman said.

'That's certainly the best time of day,' somebody said. 'when the shadows begin to lengthen the course is extremely pleasant. Oh, you know, I don't do more than five or six holes. I'm here for a rest. . . .'

Rose had not yet been cast out from the ring of talk into which she had, by a sort of miracle, been admitted. The man who was talking about golf was going to look at her and ask her: 'Do you play too sometimes?' She would answer, 'No,' but would hurriedly add: 'I shall have to take it up; everybody who plays tells me it's a most enjoyable game. . . .' Thus she would make amends for her inferiority, since maybe (and she averted her eyes from this insane hope, though she could not resist an inward smile), perhaps all was not hopeless, irremediable, between herself and them?

The man looked at her but did not open his mouth. No doubt it was quite out of the question, for him, that Rose should play golf. Indeed, he was obviously wondering why on earth she was there, taking part in the conversation.

Rose felt herself being violently ejected from the common ground; she experienced a kind of panic and tried to cling on for a second longer, just long enough to find out if it might not all be a misunderstanding, due to some involuntary movement, one of those absent-minded silences so easily mistaken for the symptoms of estrangement. She looked in vain towards her neighbours for some support; they had already forgotten her presence, they were drifting into forgetfulness as one drifts into sleep. She was being cut off from them, annihilated, cast into outer darkness; they would let her image die out within them, like a neglected lamp.

'You could quite well get to the golf course by the path along the coast I was telling you about just now,' Rose said to the young woman, with exaggerated fervour.

But these words, she realized, would not succeed in re-awakening the interest of her fellow guests, in bringing it back to herself, in fanning the dying flame which, when it was revived artificially (but would it ever revive?) would set them peering forward, shading their eyes with their hands, like sleepers suddenly awakened trying to adjust their eyes to the light, or else, like a sleepless man who, having first resigned himself to lying in the dark, ends by turning on the light and lies for a while in pensive immobility trying to recognize his own hands against the sheet, they would stare thoughtfully, for a long time, at the tablecloth and the flickering lights and shadows on it, and would not answer yet. . . .

'Yes,' Rose went on with painful sprightliness, 'you could quite well try my "escape route" in the opposite direction. . . .'

She had used this ambiguous expression deliberately, hoping thereby to arouse the suspicion of her neighbours, who seemed too much inclined to lose interest in her. She accompanied her words with a smile which she endeavoured to make enigmatic when the nearest guests turned their eyes on her once more.

'But that would be unspeakably rash!' replied the young woman in the white dress, her voice failing at the mere thought. 'Suppose the smoke should blow in our faces or the grass catch fire up to the edge of the road! Frankly, I've no desire to play with fire!'

A brief murmur of approval accompanied her final words. She had already turned her head towards her husband and, with an artificial liveliness intended to inform Rose that their conversation was at an end, began to question him eagerly about the letters that had come that morning.

The other guests, at the neighbouring tables, went on eating in silence. Perhaps suspicion was already at work in their minds, perhaps they were merely trying to discourage Rose from speaking to them again. Seeing them so intent on their food, the head waiter came up to them and, with deferential gravity, questioned them in a low voice, anticipating their wishes, signing to a waiter to bring back a dish or fill a glass or push forward a mustard-pot on the tablecloth, furtive attentions proffered in silence which the guests accepted with a nod of the head, their mouths full, pensive and as though absorbed in contemplation of some elusive truth, submitting meekly to the solemn rites of these white-clad ministrants.

During the intervals when his function consisted merely in being present and things were going smoothly at the tables, the head waiter occasionally looked at Rose. He had already guessed that she belonged to a different class from the other guests, and he had hardly waited for her to encourage him with a smile before insinuating into certain of his remarks, as he bent respectfully over her table, a note of deliberate gallantry with a hint of coarseness in it. The man was young and dark, and black hairs showed under his cuffs. Rose was aware, when she answered him, that he was staring at her teeth, and the irony of her replies concealed a certain uneasiness.

From her table, she tried to renew the smiling complicity that had thus been formed between the head waiter and herself, but this time the man remained impassive. Had he overheard the ambiguous remark she had made a moment before? had he begun to form suspicions? She was beginning to regret her imprudence; now she was not merely not admitted, she was excluded; the silence of banishment loomed over her already.

Having finished her meal, she was reluctant to get up and leave the room. Too many glances loaded with curiosity or excessive contempt would be turned on her as she passed; and what whispers, what exclamations would break out as soon as she had crossed the threshold! The thought brought sweat to her brow. And then suddenly came the reassuring, almost exalting idea: perhaps the fire was out by now.

She would go outside; she would be the first to make the discovery and she would tell nobody, for fear of compromising herself once more by spreading the news too eagerly. She would go and sit in the middle of the garden, in the spot from which the fire had been visible a short while ago, and would pretend to doze or dream or read, indifferent to everything. The others would come out: 'Look it's all over, there's no more smoke to be seen.' Rose would raise herself a little in her cane chair, turn her head, shade her eyes with her hand. 'Why, so it is,' (she would not actually say these words, her attitude would speak for her) and quickly sink into the armchair with bored languor.

She walked swiftly out of the dining room without thinking about the people who might be looking at her. The smoke from the forest fire had grown thicker, and, now that the wind had dropped, was rising straight up into the sky. Rose passed her hand over her brow: 'This is ridiculous. It's no responsibility of mine.' Ridiculous, too, to have advised the golfers to take the coast path. The fire appeared to have spread in a seaward direction and no doubt was making this path largely impassable. 'They won't fail to realize that,' Rose thought. 'They'll hold it against me.'

She was crossing the hall to go back to her room when the other guests came out of the dining room. Not one of them looked at Rose. Then she realized with peculiar force what a boon their indifference was at this juncture; once back in her room, however, her apprehensions revived.

She worked at her translation till the evening. It was the chapter in which Barbara Strauss reproaches Baldwell with having allowed her, during their journey to Shrewsbury, to 'empty out her heart'. 'During a confession the moment comes,' she says, 'when you're speaking for someone deep within you, some familiar stranger, who is finally magnetized by the terrific compulsion to put things into words – and he ungloves his hands like thunderbolts. What is most lucid in us is our silences.' They decide to go back to Shrewsbury, when Baldwell's mother, who was supposed to be still in Italy, turns up.

Until that moment Rose had not left her work table. Barbara Strauss's final words, which she had just set down, startled her from her concentration and, soon, from her immobility. 'There is always a long interval, in life, between the moment when one is wounded and the moment when one bleeds. We live unaware of this, unable to interpret that cruel unfamiliar shortness of breath which is more or less concealed under the apparently tranquil continuity of our gestures, those blank moments when the blood stream seems suspended, when one staggers dizzily on the point of passing through that door which . . .'

Rose went up to the window, which she had closed so as to keep out the sound of the fire and the sound of other people. She drew back the curtain. The big tree, in the heart of which darkness was already nesting, was waving its downy leaves. Beyond, the sea lay desolate. 'The moment when one is wounded. . . . See that pair of lovers; their hands are full of knives.' She leaned her head against the window pane: 'How lonely I am now.' It was nearly dinner time. What had happened about the forest fire?

It was going to be part of the night henceforward, with its tall flames and its flickering red glow. Rose felt as though she were going to have to appear in public in a low-cut dress on a vast nocturnal stage. With the coming of night the fire – and Rose, under suspicion of complicity – had become 'part of the show'. But whatever that might involve, it was time for her to get ready, and she went into the bathroom. She tried to turn on the light; nothing happened. She pressed the bedroom switch with no better result, and opened the door on to the passage; it was in complete darkness. She recognized the silhouette and the white apron of a chambermaid on the landing and called out to her.

'There's no current,' replied the girl, leaning over the

banister to look out for help from below, 'it's on account of the fire. . . .'

Rose went back to her room and opened the window. She leaned out to look in the direction of the forest. The sky had turned a deeper blue, with a trail of misty thunderclouds hanging there. Several people were talking on the steps outside; Rose could not follow what they were saying. She left her room again and went downstairs in the dark, clinging to the stair rail.

The reception office was lit by a candle stuck in the neck of a mineral-water bottle. The manager, a fat baldish man in a summer suit, was losing his head, clamouring for his staff, hunting for keys and papers in a blind man's frenzy. A few guests had come up to reassure their eyes at the light of the single candle.

'I ask you, gentlemen,' the manager kept saying, 'what's the sense of putting the main transformer in the middle of the forest?'

'Is it the transformer?' asked Rose who, forgetting the suspicion that her remarks during lunch might have aroused, was once more conscious of a wish to mingle cordially with other people.

'Yes, Mademoiselle,' replied the manager, 'and I've only got this one wretched candle at my disposal. So I'll have to ask you to be patient for a little. If only I dared leave the place! and not one of my staff can drive! Oh yes, there's the head waiter – but where is he? how can I find him? We ought to go and buy up a few dozen candles while they've still got them in the shops . . .'

'Well, I'll go,' Rose said. 'My car's just outside the door. How many do you need?'

She had spoken before anyone else and loud enough to be heard from the hall where the guests were now thronging, uneasy at the darkness and very hungry.

'I hardly like to accept, Mademoiselle,' the manager was saying. 'Of course it would be in everybody's interest. Really I'm quite embarrassed . . . I think that with five dozen . . .'

'Matches, too, we'll need some matches,' a delicate, quivering feminine voice spoke somewhere in the depths of the darkness.

A murmur of satisfaction quickly rippled into the furthest corners of the hall where, resigned to gloom and stupefied with waiting, several people had sunk into leather armchairs; the red tips of their cigarettes were glowing silently, as if in battle.

'Five dozen,' Rose repeated in a loud voice. 'Look here, as I read a great deal at night I'll bring six dozen. . . .'

People began to laugh; they made way for her as she went towards the door. Somebody pulled a child by the arm and it began to cry.

The town was three and a half miles away from the hotel. Rose drove very fast along the winding road, between tamarisk hedges. She hurried to the grocery where she knew there would be candles. Visitors were queueing up there. Rose took the last three dozen. People behind her protested; the shop-woman, with a deeply apologetic air, offered them storm lanterns, while Rose, deaf to their complaints, walked out of the shop.

She was sitting at the wheel again and preparing to drive off at top speed when she thought better of it. This time revenge was in her hands. All the guests in the hotel were looking forward to her return with eager confidence even perhaps with a certain affectionate emotion. They were all intently awaiting the result of this unselfish act, the news of which had flown round in the dark. Rose's name would have been circulated or, which was even more likely to ensure her fame, like those photographs in the papers that bring much greater glory than the useless repetitions of the reporters' stories, the description of her person, of the way she usually dressed, of the position of her table in the dining room.

It would have been a real blunder to put a premature stop, by a too hasty return, to all that buzz of talk which, like water flooding into a lock, was suddenly drowning Rose's loneliness and raising her to the common level. She must leave other people time, amidst that darkness which made it easier to yield

to the natural and simple impulses of the heart, to accomplish
their act of silent contrition and the process of rehabilitation
which consisted in describing Rose, the colour of her hair, her
dress, and in giving their sanction (she dared not yet say
giving their blessing) to her existence.

She lit a cigarette, amused herself for a few minutes watching
the bewildered holiday-makers running about on the little
square, meeting, handing one another a few candles, parting
again, some hurrying towards their dwellings which seemed
swallowed up in the depths of night, the others trying to inter-
cept some man who was scurrying past carrying a long candle,
as though he had robbed a vestry, to ask him where they could
still be got. Then she started her engine again and drove gently
along to about a hundred yards from the hotel.

Then she had to brake as sharply as if some obstacle had
sprung up in front of her: the hotel windows had just lit up.
All around, the lights were on again in the villas, even that
naked bulb hanging out of doors over a porch, under the flat
enamelled corolla of its shade, into which were dipping tiny
white, transparent moths to which only their flight gave
substance.

Rose stayed there, at the wheel of her stationary car, appalled.
From where she was (she had turned out the sidelights and
headlights so as not to betray her presence) she could see,
against the illuminated background of the great bay windows
of the hotel lounge, guests who had come to life again and
were moving about with joyous animation in the light of
lamps and chandeliers, a light clearer and brighter than ever, as
dazzling as the light that greets one's awakening. The wind
blew a snatch of music to her ears. She felt herself forgotten,
mocked by the mirth of which she could see the signs on the
other side of the dark garden.

No, she could not possibly go back into the hall with her
bundles of candles clasped to her bosom, she could not appear
in front of all those assembled people with this ridiculous
booty, this devaluated merchandise, which the manager would

take from her and pay her for with the ironic consolation: 'After all, they may come in useful sometime. . . .'

She could not possibly endure the smiles that would greet her as she crossed the hall, the comments of "Tough luck!' that would emphasize her failure as if, far from accomplishing an altruistic deed, she had been taking part in some competition in which nobody else had ever been interested. Nor could she endure hearing someone say: 'A bit late!' with a shade of reproach – after all, they had waited for her in the darkness! Why hadn't she left the job of going to buy candles to one of the hotel staff? such people knew their job, though you might feel it your vocation. . . .

The high garden wall of some villa ran alongside the road just where Rose had drawn up. She got out of her car, holding her packets of candles, then changed her mind and laid a couple of candles on the seat: the light might fail again, one of these days. She crossed the road and threw the packets of candles, one after the other, over the garden wall.

Now she could go back to the hotel nonchalantly, empty-handed. She would look at the assembled guests and allow them to guess that she was thinking of something else, she would give them the impression that she had been the first to forget the incident, the sudden darkness and her mission. If the manager asked her any questions, (but was it certain that he would ask any?) she would emerge from her dream, with raised eyebrows. 'Candles? Oh yes, of course; there weren't any left. . . .' She would utter these words in such an offhand, indifferent manner that nobody would know if she had been in vain to try and get candles or if, taking shrewd advantage of the return of the light, she had spent her time in a bar or, better still, at some mysterious rendezvous.

She carefully parked her car in the hotel garage, tidied her hair with the help of the mirror and then went into the garden. She was going up the steps to the porch when the lights flickered and went out. Cries of disappointment filled the hall.

'That light was too bright to last, it was abnormally bright,' a woman kept repeating with despair in her voice.

'We must have overloaded another circuit. I guessed that would happen,' a man said, close to Rose. He brushed against her: 'And now I can't think where I put my glass of Scotch. . . .'

Rose stood motionless. Why had she been in such a hurry to get rid of the candles? Couldn't she have left them in the car and given them back to the shopkeeper next morning? She was always yielding to these movements of panic, these exorcizing gestures intended to keep illusion free from the contamination of truth.

'No sign of her,' said a man not far from Rose.

He heaved a sigh right up against her, almost into her hair. She heard the click of a lighter being opened and she moved off towards the far end of the hall, where the hotel's single candle was burning itself out, its flame dancing on anxious faces, hollowed out by shadows. She would have to see it through. She drew near the light. The manager recognized her.

'At last!' he cried, leaping out of his chair. 'Have you got them?'

'I couldn't get any,' answered Rose.

'How's that, Mademoiselle?' the manager cried. 'But you went off at once! I've just rung up the Select, they set off after us, their car wouldn't start, and they've got some! *They've got some,*' he repeated, accenting the last words with bitterness.

'I don't know what to say,' stammered Rose, while muttered protests rose around her.

The manager chose not to answer her; he ran his fingers under his collar with a grimace of annoyance, casting his eyes round him.

'I'll go myself. I know everybody in the town. It would be the limit if . . .'

He darted off in the darkness, sweeping aside, with both arms, the shadowy figures in his path.

'When one's as incompetent as that, one stays put and doesn't offer to help,' said a man not far from Rose in a very loud voice.

Some women nearby endorsed his remark.

'Oh, so it was that woman,' one of them remarked. 'I thought she was one of the staff.'

Rose groped her way towards the stair; she was beating a retreat.

She still fostered a last remnant of hope, as she climbed the stairs in the darkness, accompanied by the sound of that menacing murmur, reverberating in the hollow well of the stair; the manager had friends in town, he would bring back candles or lamps, or else the electric current would be restored. The incident, and Rose's failure, would soon be forgotten. Then, suddenly, she felt ashamed of her weakness. She discovered a fierce delight in wishing that nothing might come to weaken the hostility that the other guests now felt towards her. She had tried hard enough to overcome their indifference! nothing had worked; at the first door she had pushed open, at the first step she'd taken she had met the black blast of hatred. Love of others was like a treacherous house whose welcome concealed endless snares. . . . On the landing, the beam from a pocket torch shone into her face.

'You'll lose your way, Mademoiselle, or at any rate you'll go into the wrong room. . . .'

She recognized the sneering voice of the head waiter. He seemed reluctant to lower his torch.

'You're dazzling me,' murmured Rose. 'Please show me the way to my room instead.'

'Why d'you want to go and shut yourself up all alone in the dark?' he said brusquely, switching off his torch. Then he bent over the banisters and swiftly switched it on again, flashing a beam of light down to the ground floor: 'Look at that swarm of them. . . .'

Below, tragic faces, upturned, were for a brief second exposed to the hard glare.

'Don't they look like damned souls?'

'What's this, what's this?' a man called out angrily from the bottom of the stair well.

The head waiter had put out his light and was leaning against the wall. Rose took one step in the direction of her room.

'Cigarette?' the man asked, striking a light from his lighter so that she could see the packet he was holding out to her.

She took a cigarette and lit it at the flame. Her hand was shaking a little.

'I saw you stop your car at the edge of the road just now, I was up in my room. Why did you switch off the headlights, it was very risky for yourself and others,' the head waiter said in his ironic voice.

'That's my private little mystery,' Rose answered. 'You're too inquisitive.'

She blushed in the darkness. Those words, 'my private little mystery', seemed to imply some erotic ambiguity, suggesting the coquettish prelude to a sexual encounter in which secrecy enhances temptation.

'You needn't be afraid,' the man said, suddenly lowering his voice. 'I shan't say a word to anyone. It'll be between us two; it'll be our secret. . . .'

He had taken a step towards her. His hand slid up her arm. She felt herself growing dizzy in her immobility; she suddenly jerked backwards in the darkness. 'No,' she murmured, 'no. . . .' She realized it was blackmail.

'You may say what you please to whomever you please,' she answered him coldly. 'What can you be thinking of? Now let me pass; I have to go down again.'

'Pardon me,' said the head waiter, reverting immediately to his most professional voice. 'I'll give you a light.'

He directed the beam from his torch on to the steps as Rose began to walk down them, shifting it to follow her downward towards the ground floor. With exaggerated considerateness, he kept calling out to her in loud tones: 'Can you see, Mademoiselle? Keep closer to the rail! Careful of the edge of the carpet, careful of the landing now!' From time to time he pointed the beam of light not on the stairs but on Rose's face, making it dance over her bosom and arms, lavishing noisy advice on her the while. In the utter darkness of the hotel, Rose's downward journey over the heads of the assembled guests, waiting there helplessly for light, assumed a solemn, public character, while the head waiter, up above, redoubled his attentions: 'Gently, gently, Mademoiselle, we're nearly there. . . .'

'Oh, leave me alone,' cried Rose, 'I'm not a helpless cripple '

He was making a laughing stock of her. The guests understood this after a few seconds and began to laugh very loud; somebody shouted: 'Here comes our little ray of sunshine!' Out of sheer boredom, the men must have drunk a good deal already; the barman had brought his bottles and glasses to the counter of the reception desk. Loud mutterings, ironic and hostile, greeted Rose as she reached the ground floor.

She ran to the garage to fetch the two candles that she had left in her car. For the space of one second she felt strongly impelled to escape, but she could not abandon her luggage nor leave without paying what she owed, and besides, where could she take refuge in this abysmal darkness? And after all what did she care for the hostility of other people? She would try to forget this sequence of absurd happenings. In a few hours daylight, and with it freedom, would be restored to the world. She felt an urgent need to work at her translation, to get back to Barbara at the point where she, too, was contemplating suicide, without despair and without anger, 'purely from politeness towards herself, so as not to inflict too much . . .

She hid the two candles in her handbag. She made her way into the hall, haunted with impatient shadows, with voices grown shriller, and glided towards the stairs. When she reached the landing where, a short while before, the head waiter had been standing, terror gripped her heart. Was he waiting for her? She thought she heard him breathing in the darkness and she struck a match. She was close to her own room. She locked the door behind her and groped her way to the window to close the shutters and draw the curtains. A car drove into the hotel garden; it was the manager coming back. Some guests hurried towards him; she heard the door of the car being slammed.

'Two candles,' said the manager wearily, 'not a single one more, gentlemen. You see me at my wits' end. As for the current, we shan't get it back till tomorrow. . . .'

After drawing the curtains, Rose lighted the two candles, which she stuck in a little pool of wax on the marble of her bedside table.

If Barbara thinks of killing herself when the interference of Baldwell's mother wrecks their plan of going back to Shrewsbury, it is not merely because the events of the last three days have committed her to a course of action which is a dead-end. These events have, in actual fact, provided a sort of relief. Always the same time-lag in life, between the moment when one is wounded . . .

'Oh, just look, there's a light under the door,' said a loud voice in the passage.

'Good Lord,' exclaimed another man, 'it's unbelievable!'

'She's taken everybody in. She's taken us in. She's made fools of us! But whatever did she hope to gain from it?' said a woman's plaintive voice.

'She'll hear us,' somebody whispered.

'So what?'

How many of them were there? Rose lit a cigarette at the flame of one of the candles, settled her back against the pillow and took up her pen again: '*Michael, pourquoi m'avoir laissé parler? Barbara plonge son visage dans ses mains, pétrit ce masque de douleur qui est, depuis si longtemps déjà, son visage fidèle . . .*'

Reading the sentence over, she found it weak. She would have to tackle it again.

'I think it's disgusting! quite unpardonable!' cried the man who, a short while before, had been the first to speak.

'Please, Louis, keep calm!' a woman said. 'It's not worth your getting angry with such a person. . . .'

'I'd like to ask her a few explanations,' another man hissed.

'What's happening?' other voices, further off, called out.

Some more guests who had come on to the landing went up

to Rose's room. The passage was soon filled with hostile mutterings.

'I've a strong desire to knock at that door! I can't think why I shouldn't,' said one man.

'No, no,' some women cried.

Overcome by panic, Rose leapt from her bed. Now they were going to break in her door, insult her, maybe strike her. She took refuge by the window. In the garden, other guests were talking.

'Look, the curtain's moved a little; you can see, the room's full of light!' somebody shouted.

A shower of small pebbles hit the shutters.

'Robert, I forbid you!' a woman cried. 'Drop that stone!'

Catcalls sounded, as at the theatre. 'I must put out the light,' Rose said to herself. Her legs were shaking. 'I must put it out,' she repeated to herself without stirring. Those voices in the passage, where anger was swelling, those voices and catcalls in the garden. She was hemmed in. . . . She pressed the palms of her hands against her ears and went to blow out the candles. All around her, close to her, exclamations rang out.

Rose did not hear them. Standing in the middle of her room, now quite dark, she went on holding her head in her hands. Sobs shook her breast. 'They'll always be against me, always! I shall always be alone! Oh, why did I leave you at Viareggio last year? Oh, why aren't you beside me?'

She had suddenly discovered her love, and running through it, that thin cruel line, that narrow, deep wound which, a whole year afterwards had begun to sting afresh, revived by the salt sea air, amidst the howling of the wind. . . .

translated by Jean Stewart

The Asylum

THE ASYLUM stood a few miles from the city, on the fringe of a working-class suburb overlooking a plain that heaved gently, like a page being turned, a page that has been read, emptied of meaning, grey with oblivion. No one will ever turn it. A few very tall trees shaded the asylum buildings, their tollhouse isolation, which a flag over the entrance signalled to whom it might concern. In the distance the wind was pushing clouds.

Sometimes it was a heavy summer day, sometimes a rainy afternoon, rarely a snow-speckled dawn, but always the same sky which ignored the seasons; it lodged madness in the slightly livid light which bathes the pictures of very old Flemish painters and gives them their lasting finish.

First there had been the interminable ride along tree-lined avenues, through low-roofed towns. Then the arrival at the asylum gates, and – after so many days of endless passing through a thousand doors – seeing them open before her would merely have provoked a mute acquiescence in Rose if, at that very moment, a man in a white smock had not bent down, with the cruel meticulousness of sanity, to remove a pebble that was blocking the door. Was the torture to begin all over again? Had they all, already, taken up their old positions?

'You'll see, we're going to behave very well,' now said a woman, also all in white. 'We'll go to the dormitory. But first we'll change our clothes.'

The use of the first person plural created an exasperating climate of false complicity. At last they went out into the park. Women with untidy hairdos, all in blue dresses, daydreamed or chattered, came, went or just sat under the trees.

It was towards the end of June that Rose Schmidt, locked in a city ambulance, passed through the asylum gates. Seasons have a way of seeming endless, even though they have hardly begun. The asylum summer, with its leaves cutting almost black into the light of the sky, was as rigid, as permanent as destiny: a summer of iron lances. They slipped a hand under your arm to help you walk.

'Rose Schmidt,' murmured the nurse between finely drawn lips to direct her attention while entering Rose's name in the register.

Her husband had not come with her and one might have thought that, by registering Rose under her maiden name, the nurse was condemning her forever to his absence. Actually, as Rose found out later, the nurse was merely complying with a regulation established during the last century, which stipulated that, upon entering the asylum, all married women reverted to their maiden names.

'Rose Schmidt, born September eighteen, nineteen twenty-two,' repeated the nurse who was making up a file, consulting certificates that seemed to have appeared from nowhere, 'September eighteen, nineteen twenty-two . . .'

Driven by feminine curiosity she scrutinized the age of each newcomer as though she were trying to reassure herself of her own relative immunity or, at least, discover proof of some reprieve which might have been granted her; she finally emerged from her indifference.

'So we're thirty,' she said, raising her eyes, 'thirty.'

'Miss . . .' stammered Rose.

'Brun, my name is Mrs Brun,' said the nurse with a kind of snake charmer's insistence.

Always someone to pull us towards conversation, this fluid place where we do not wish to go – always someone who has been hanging around our silence for a long, long time and who, all of a sudden, starts playing the 'transparent mask'.

'Miss . . . ' repeated Rose with a bewildered voice, or a forgotten voice.

And her hand sketched a vague gesture against her hip. Out of reach, reality was already fleeing.

'Let's go; let's go,' said another nurse who was standing behind Rose and whom she had not seen come in.

They hurried out into the park.

While they were dressing her in the madwomen's uniform, after the shower, Rose kept her head obstinately turned towards the barred window, towards the tops of the trees, motionless in the light of the sky. It was the only way of staying separate, of showing them that she was letting them take this sort of docility like another blouse. Allowing oneself to be dressed in blue was a way of accepting the fact that one was being stripped once more: they were dressing her in absence.

They made her lift one arm, both arms, one leg, the other leg. And every time, a back bowed down before her, but in a treacherous pose – the face of the woman, slightly raised, with a frozen smile – a back to lean on. Now both arms had to be raised again together; Rose's eyes did not leave the sky.

'Look at her, standing there like a recruit passing his physical,' baa-ed a voice behind her.

They threw her a shirt and underpants in rough undyed linen, a blue-and-white-checkered blouse and skirt. No stockings. She thrust her feet – ice cold from the tile floor – into list slippers. She was still holding herself very straight.

'Put your head down!' yelled a nurse.

She obeyed. Impatient hands rummaged through her hair,

4

braided it, knotted it into a bun. They gave her two dull black combs with uneven teeth. Rose let the combs drop to the floor. She was finally breaking down; she had tried too hard up to now. Her legs buckled under her; her knees and hands touched the tiles. But she did not stretch out; she guessed that then they would carry her off through more doors, and afterwards one can never be sure to find them all again, you know, one wanders forever in empty, faintly echoing halls. . . .

'Do you think she ought to be put to bed?' a woman asked, obsequiously eager. She had come up, dressed in the same blue and white as Rose. 'Look, she's squatting there like a toad.'

'No, but you may take her out to get some air in the court-yard,' replied the nurse.

The woman bent down and grabbed Rose under the arms.

'Come on! Stand up!' she cried, already drunk with her authority.

Rose had recovered from her faintness. She stood up. The woman in blue took her hand. She was an old woman with a flat face; the skin of her cheeks glistened like the new skin of someone who has been burned, but it was yellow and deeply lined. She had a slightly jerky walk that strained hard for dignity, and this aimless excursion through corridors that all looked alike became for Rose – after the exactions, the recent scoldings, the chaos of gestures and words – what horse trainers or men of the ring call 'the cooling-off period', a slow-motion walk, almost dreamlike, but during which a kind of 'stepping', blood-shot eyes still unable to see, a sobbing movement of the shoulders, betray the long disaster of violence, the un-redeemed effort.

'One-two; one-two,' murmured the old woman at every second step, caught in the majesty of the rite.

But the slippers were too loose for Rose's feet. She stumbled.

'Pick up your feet!' ordered the old woman.

The spell was broken. Rose hung her head, staring at her veined feet in the formless slippers, fascinated by their penitent nakedness.

They had entered a great hall, furrowed by long marble tables with benches lined up on either side. A stale odour rose from the iron sink along the wall. Women came and went, with nothing to do, living out their patience.

One of them came up. 'A new one?' she asked.

'Yes,' answered the old woman, 'and I'm teaching her to march.'

'You're teaching her to march,' said the other woman pensively. 'I'm not surprised. The bastards!' she yelled, shaking her fist at the ceiling, 'that's all they're after: to make us march, the whole bunch of us, in ranks, just like an army. Why don't they make us goose-step, while they're at it?'

Clumsy with anger she did a brief goose step before the women who had gathered around Rose. Suddenly a strand of grey hair fell into her eyes. She stopped, put a hand to her forehead and disappeared among the spectators.

'Don't sob like that, oh, don't sob like that,' someone kept saying behind the crowd where an invisible woman was sobbing, doubled over against a wall of backs.

'If you want my opinion, it's more like little short steps, dance-hall style,' said a tough-looking girl, pushing her way into the circle.

She rolled her hips suggestively. There was laughter.

'All right, ladies! What's going on?' shouted a nurse from the end of the room.

The sound of keys, jangling as she ran, announced her arrival.

'I don't like crowds; you know very well I don't like crowds. Out into the yard, all of you!'

She came up to Rose who had not moved.

'I said: all of you!' she said slowly, chewing each word.

'But he is going to come!' cried Rose. How could they mistake her for one of the others? 'He is going to come!' she repeated with desperate conviction.

'Then go and wait for him outside,' said the nurse, giving her a push.

Outside, a wide stretch of bare ground led to the yellowing lawn, the sterile earth of courtyards, whitewashed with dryness, hard like gritty cement. After a step or two Rose felt the gravel coming through her shoes. She stopped in the full sun. Around her, women were taking off their slippers to empty them, lifting a rough, grey foot, like a horse being shod, Then, with an air of urgency, they started out again, towards some corner of the lawn, to go on chewing the grass of uselessness,

There were some very old patients with snow-white hair, who no longer even had the energy to be crazy, lulled by senility as though it were a cure. Their veined hands on their knees, they sat on the stone benches, while – armed with their nails and their curt words of abuse – the madwomen paced back and forth in front of them like a tribe of daughters-in-law.

The city prisons had sent several inmates with dark complexions and brooding, oval faces who sprawled in the grass, their lips sealed by stony silence. They stared straight ahead, defying the brightest sun, with the insolence of gypsies along the highways.

Further on, a home for retarded girls had sent four or five seventeen- or eighteen-year-olds, who wore curlers of candy-box ribbon in their blonde hair and were beating time with their hands, giggling out of gap-toothed mouths. And the dwarf was there, like an upturned face; you didn't see her; you didn't hear her come; she was there, in your skirts, right up against you, like a ball which has been thrown, stopping, always revealing the same questioning face, large and kinky, with a voice coming up from under your feet. And above it all the sobbing of the invisible woman, and the words of her comforter:

'Martha, Martha, don't sob like that, don't sob like that!'

A climbing plant on the sunny asylum wall. . . .

A woman of about sixty with almost snow-white hair and a soft, worn face came up to Rose. 'You've just arrived?' she asked. 'Of course,' she went on with a smile, 'that was a silly question. I'm fully aware that you weren't here a minute ago; I would have noticed you. My name is Mrs Mingot; yes, even here, they call me Mrs . . . I used to teach abroad. I just arrived myself . . . two years ago, that is. But you'll see, time does not pass here. Look how new we are.'

Rose looked about her, as the old woman's gesture demanded. She had not retained much from her rapid words, except this idea of newness, which the old woman ordered her to verify. The women came and went, or sat in a kind of primal freedom that Rose had never seen anywhere before. In this narrow space nothing beckoned to them but themselves. Coming up to Rose, they assumed singular importance, all buttoned to the neck in blue linen, armed with all their signs, all their weapons, intact as on the first day.

'What is your name?' asked Mrs Mingot.

'Rose.' (Are you quite sure? an inner voice murmured in her ear.) 'He is going to come, isn't he!' she exclaimed, desperate with the feeling that everything, even her first name, might escape her in this state of loneliness.

'Who is going to come?' asked Mrs Mingot.

Rose didn't answer. She had to be careful with this name, this last certitude. She must always carry it deep inside her, make it appear slowly in the hollow of her clasped hands, in the loneliness of the nights, rouse it again, crush it with her mouth, involve it endlessly in this debauchery of the heart, this salty drunkenness of grief, paid with black sheep, with the return of a morning that one should not have lived.

'In any case, today is not visitors' day,' pursued Mrs Mingot with acid gaiety. 'Visitors come on Sundays and Thursdays, and besides, you've only arrived. Give yourself time to catch your breath. . . .''

One Sunday morning, long, long ago, they had gone boating. This image now reappeared in Rose's mind. A slight wind had risen in the asylum leaves. It reminded her of the rushing water of a lively stream.

'You're not answering, you seem mute,' said Mrs Mingot.

'Do you at least hear what I am saying? Look at me, please, I'm here, I'm talking to you!'

She was now standing before Rose with half-distended mouth and a hurt look in her eyes.

'I so want to see him,' stammered Rose painfully.

Reassured, her companion said with eagerness, 'You'll see him, don't worry, you'll see him very soon.''

She had taken Rose's arm and was pulling her towards the end of the courtyard.

'Okay; let's get this blasted gravel cleaned up!' she shouted to her retinue.

No one heard her. But then, had she really spoken?

'Come, let's go and sit against the wall in the sun,' she said to Rose. 'We'll have a quiet little chat. You'll be my friend.'

'You see,' she began, once they had settled down on the ground, 'they come. . . . No, don't look for them in the distance. Understand me, I mean it is their function to come, now that we have been exiled. They leave the city on Sundays and Thursdays. Apparently there are extra buses running all up and down this road of compassion. They arrive, bored or distracted, with their guilty consciences, my poor dear, with their shame and pity, and a handful of sugar in their pockets. My only son got tired of it. You'll see, in winter all this is full of mud. One wades ankle-deep in sociology. And we, all dressed in blue, looking all alike. . . . It defies perseverance, it would even defy passion! One day they stop coming. Who is to blame? We died before they did!'

Mrs Mingot talked on and on. Occasionally she stopped, staring into the distance, her hands open on her knees. At those moments Rose looked at her with curiosity and then once more, closing her eyes, she was swept towards the sky where her lament stretched itself in the wind. Where was he? Why were they so far away from each other? Why?

"How cold it has suddenly become!' said Mrs Mingot. 'Look, Rose, it's actually freezing. . . .'

It was towards evening. She was holding a dead leaf

between her fingers, delicate lace. The sun was going down.

'It is freezing,' Rose repeated submissively.

She saw a delicate frost cover the trembling leaf and all around, the patinaed stone of the walls, the hardened earth over which the evening was spreading a pale foam of light. She sat among the silent women. She savoured the quiet of the hour and the fairy scene of the frost transforming the last light. When the bell rang, she rose calmly, and took a place in the lines before the door that a nurse was unbolting.

'Follow me, don't lose me, Rose! You may even hold my hand,' said Mrs Mingot, pulling her into the dining hall through the flood of women.

Large aluminium pots sat on stoves behind a hedge of nurses.

'Over here! Over here!' called Mrs Mingot, running between the long tables.

She sat down before Rose could join her, holding both hands on the bench next to her to save the space which she intended for her new companion.

'If you sit near the stoves you'll be served first,' she said to Rose who had just sat down beside her. 'I've always been partial to priority, and besides, this cold has made me ravenous. . . . Smell that: blood sausage tonight; every Wesdneday, burst blood sausage. . . .'

Her smile changed to a pout, but she had already forgotten her disgust.

'Treguel!' she cried, staring across the table.

The girl called Treguel was one of those who had been dancing rounds a little earlier, in the sun. Now she was waiting for her plate to be filled . . . with her tin spoon stuck into her mouth.

'Treguel, will you stop that!' cried Mrs Mingot, jumping to her feet.

Nurses were already busy at the end of the table; Mrs Mingot turned to them.

'Ladies!' she shouted.

But the hubbub was too great; no one heard her.

'Ladies!' Mrs Mingot shouted again.

Rose hung her head, petrified with fear of a scandal. Up to now she had more or less passed unnoticed. For weeks she had forced herself to be docile, to tiptoe, to keep quiet. She knew that in this world of punishment in which she had placed herself this was the only way, for her, to 'reach the door', to be with him again.

Two of the nurses had heard Mrs Mingot's call. They came over. 'Look! Look at her!' said Rose's companion. 'And she's capable of swallowing it. My throat is all in knots just looking at her. . . .'

'That's enough now, Treguel!' yelled one of the nurses, tapping her finger against her powdered cheek.

The girl opened round child's eyes and slowly withdrew the spoon from her mouth.

'Dirty squealer!' said a dark woman at Rose's right. The nurses had gone away.

'A little advice, dearie,' continued the woman, pulling Rose by the sleeve, 'watch out for Mrs Mingot. She squeals. You don't believe it, huh?'

'Leave her alone!' yelled a fat woman with pale cheeks and fluttering eyelids from the other side of the table. 'She's frightened. She just got here. Can't you see she's frightened?'

Rose hung her head. There was silence. A ladle of blackish soup was being poured in Rose's plate.

'Lentil soup again!' cried the dark-haired woman.

She didn't feel like eating and clanked her spoon down. One elbow on the table she leaned her cheek on her hand, with a sulky mouth. But soon she got bored. 'So you're still frightened,' she asked suddenly, again pulling Rose by the sleeve. Rose had just decided to lift her spoon. The soup spilled all over the table and dripped on her dress.

'Oh! This is impossible!' cried Mrs Mingot who, busy as she was emptying her plate, had seen what had happened.

She raised her hand to catch the eye of one of the nurses and snapped her fingers. This time a murmur of disapproval went up all around the table. The heads of all the women, secretly attached to the same body, welded together at bottom, in the depths of insanity, sitting on their knotted flesh like a king of rats,[1] turned towards Rose and her companion. The murmuring grew louder.

Standing in the middle of the wave, Mrs Mingot was imploring a white form. The nurse stopped trying to find the culprit and beat her hands together sharply several times. The women calmed down. The nurse leaned over Rose's shoulder.

'Look here, you're not going to start trouble the minute you arrive,' she said to her. 'Come on now, eat your soup!'

She pushed a brimming spoon against Rose's lips. Round and obstinate, the metal spoon had the weight and taste of a tongue depressor. Fighting a feeling of nausea, Rose swallowed, but she hurriedly put the spoon down the minute the nurse – who had put it in her hand – turned her back.

All the women were staring at her, and their joined looks spelled out that label she was so afraid of. What did these women want? Why was she among them? Why wasn't he there? Suddenly she had become the 'trouble maker', and they were pointing at her, repeating her name up and down the tables, and each time her name met a blank face, and turned new eyes against her, staring at her, and Mrs Mingot wouldn't speak to her: she couldn't afford to expose herself; she let Rose bear this dreaded notoriety.

The nurse clapped her hands again. Rose got up with the others. No one was looking at her any more. The rites of the community made sudden claims on all the women, and this nocturnal rite had a special solemnity.

'Stand close to me, Rose,' Mrs Mingot whispered in her ear. 'Hold my hand tight, no, tighter than that! Ah, you don't know how to hold on. There, I'll hold your hand. We don't talk on the way to bed.'

[1] An abnormality: a litter of rats born with bodies joined, usually by a single tail.

4*

In ranks they climbed the wide stone steps to the dormitory. In the white tiled corridors the river of women flowed almost noiselessly, uniform, broken only here and there by an arm stretched out as though trying to grip the wall, but finding only a smooth, fleeing plane, it remained suspended a moment in a gesture of farewell. Although the corridors were still lighted, small blue night bulbs were already burning over each door.

They entered a sort of hygienic cloister lined with white-painted beds. In spots the paint was chipped. An iron chair stood beside each bed. The turned-down part of the sheet hid almost all of the blanket, reaching to the foot of the bed. The asylum sheets were exceptionally large, no one knew exactly why, but their extraordinary size never ceased to be disturbing. One felt that one was sleeping in these sheets by suspended sentence, diverting them from their original destination (suggested by a slight odour of formaldehyde): operating rooms, linen-lined bath tubs, ice wraps, morgue shrouds. One did not live in them. Hard and stiff, they surrounded a sleep that was entirely wrapped up in itself. 'Well, you're not too badly placed,' said Mrs Mingot to Rose whom a nurse had just shown to her bed. 'You're next to Gertrude, and on your left you have the little spoon eater. Tomorrow I'll arrange to get the bed next to yours.'

She waved a hurried goodbye just as the nurse who had gone to the door and turned with a stern look was about to tell her to get back to her place. The women undressed hastily and slipped into their beds without putting on nightgowns to replace their grey linen shirts. Only one of them cried out, one short, sharp cry, like those that rise from a birdhouse or from trees when night falls with a noise of ruffled wings.

'Tsk! Tsk! Tsk!' clicked the nurse with the tip of her tongue.

'Shut up, Roubillot!' yelled someone.

'Tsk! Tsk! Tsk!' went the nurse again, standing at the door, waiting to turn off the light.

An electric switch snapped and the half-light reigned, bluish and filled with sighs, more terrible for those who, at the bottom of their constant fright, anticipated this daily execution that condemned them to suffering until morning, less kind than darkness to those who were tormented mostly by daylight phantoms.

On the next morning and the days that followed, Rose, accompanied by Mrs Mingot, returned to her screen of light, to that sunny place along the wall where, on the first evening, the chill of the depths had taken them by surprise.

'He is coming, surely he'll come today,' Rose repeated each time Mrs Mingot forced her out of silence. Should I have let him come to me, the first time? It was evening, I was scared of every bush, although I kept laughing, and we were still a hundred yards from the boat. It all happened yesterday, only yesterday. And we'll begin again!

'Sh,' said Mrs Mingot, 'shhhhh! Be quiet, Rose, don't say a word. That's from the opera, "The Dragoons of Villars". At the Red Cross I had a cook who used to sing all day long. His name was Ruprecht. He sang in German. I know German; Russian, too. . . .'

They were sitting on the ground; Rose kept silent and listened to her companion's endless monologue. Mrs Mingot unrolled her past, image after image of a far-away reality of which Rose began to be aware again. All the human feelings: first pity ('Just think, that was in nineteen forty-three, pity was dressed in red'), then goodness ('never returned, carried off in the coat of a begging thief'), love, ah yes, love, but also maternal love, anger, fear, hatred. 'The whole long list, see,' Mrs Mingot said very often, 'let me tell you. . . .'

Now she was talking of bodily miseries: cold; but it was very hard for her to call up the notion of cold sitting there against that burning wall: 'You saw how it was, yesterday, and this is June! I'm sure if you dug into the ground here you'd find frost, just like they find coal in other places. That's what makes me think that something must have happened, that we are perhaps no longer alive,' she whispered with sinister delight: '. . . not altogether living, not altogether flesh.' She also talked of fatigue, of hunger; and while, a little earlier, the description of love and pity had not moved Rose, the idea of hunger brought light to her eyes. The asylum meals were skimpy.

'At the Red Cross canteen, when they boiled potatoes, they always mashed them with a big pounder. Of course no milk. But to make up for it, lots of fat. Ah! And I can tell you: lots of fat!'

'And bread? What about bread?' asked Rose in a slightly hoarse voice.

At last she was talking sense. Smiling Mrs Mingot tipped her white head back against the hot wall and let Rose wait for an answer.

'The bread was supplied by the commissary. Biscuit. Careful now: in the exact sense of the term: twice baked. It made the crust thick and crunchy. The ration was a loaf per person: all you could eat, that is. . . .'

'I'm hungry,' murmured Rose.

Mrs Mingot leaned over her: 'When he comes, the one you miss so much, he'll bring you bread, all sorts of goodies. That's all they come for. The dead must be fed. But, to be quite frank with you, I don't think he'll come. It's too far, you see, too far, and besides, to get here he might have to cross a river, and no bridges, all kinds of obstacles. And besides, who knows? Do you deserve his visit? Perhaps you've been unfaithful, nasty? You're not listening!'

No, Rose wasn't listening.

'Come, we'll go in,' said Mrs Mingot dejectedly, and took her arm. 'This heat is killing me.'

Dodging the nurses, they slipped into the building and walked slowly down the white corridors.

'Here, over here!' whispered Mrs Mingot, who had gone ahead of Rose and had stopped in front of a window. 'Come look!'

There was Section Three, invisible from anywhere else, so well hidden, so secret that this window opening upon it, exactly like all the other windows that lighted the corridor, seemed pierced by a sharper sun. In Section Three lived the wilder cases.

'They call them "disturbed",' said Mrs Mingot. 'Look at them! I sometimes have the impression that they're calling me. Look, that one who is holding out her arms as though you were her child. Don't turn your head away! Believe me, they are the mothers of revelation. Oh! I feel so sorry for them. So terribly sorry! They feel everything, they suffer everything, everything goes through them, all the stakes, all the words, all the knives that get stuck into living flesh all over the place . . . Look, they're gathering. Why yes, they're giving them soup . . . Soup, just like that, at five o'clock in the afternoon! Rose, I have a funny feeling, come on, let's get out of here! Something is going on. I bet they're getting ready to transfer them somewhere tonight, *abtransportieren*, you know what I mean, come on, let's go!'

Rose remained motionless. The small courtyard in front of the Section Three building was now deserted. A very high wire mesh closed it in like a bird house. There was white sun everywhere. A woman came out into the light and then (probably they were all still there?) ran back in and the façade closed again on the drama of the besieged, on a final silence, pitched very high at the peak of a scream.

'What are you doing here?' a nurse asked Mrs Mingot as she was passing with her antiseptic odour, jangling keys and powdered cheeks. 'I was afraid she was getting too much sun,' answered Mrs Mingot smiling. 'You know she's not well yet,' she added in a low voice, pointing to Rose. 'A little while ago, outside, I thought she was going to start screaming any moment. . . .'

'Really?'

The nurse came up to Rose.

'Rose Schmidt, lift up your head, let me see your eyes,' she said gently, taking Rose by the arm.

Rose looked at her squarely. The nurse decided to smile as

though hoping to tame her, and finally was the first to turn her eyes away.

'All right, back outside!' she told Mrs Mingot dryly before walking off.

Every morning it was the same with the doctor on duty. Even he couldn't stand for long the painful look with which Rose answered every human gesture. He couldn't be blamed for this incarceration, which the most superficial clinical observation amply justified, nor for the illness he was labouring to cure, and yet he turned his eyes away, feeling suddenly responsible, in the chalky morning light, for this nakedness, this hurt, this loneliness.

They had to get up at six o'clock. They swallowed their bowl of malt, ate their slice of dry bread and stayed seated in the dining room waiting for the sun to light the yard. Among them those who underwent daily treatment waited for the nurse's call. Rose didn't know whether or not she, too, might be called and from the first day she had joined this silent, badly defined minority, composed of slightly haggard women who sat at the table, making their hand slide slowly over the wood, interminably, untiringly treading, far from themselves, furtive messages of fear. Near them, Mrs Mingot was silent, her eyes large with waiting.

'If they call me, I won't budge,' she had said to Rose. 'They'll be obliged to carry me in. And then, goodbye life, goodbye love. . . .'

The large glass door at the end of the room was going to open on one of those early-morning destinies that never brought you anything worthwhile. Isn't it disturbing that people on the other side of the walls are already up at this hour, putting cloths on tables?

The call was slow in coming, the sun slow in shining over the walls, the women remained silent, pacified by fear. And then came the moment when, in the sky, powers changed, night balanced day. Tics slackened, nerves relaxed. It was the moment when inner voices no longer shouted threats, when breathing eased, when knotted throats untied themselves, when an interminable thread of saliva ran from idiot mouths, when the feeble did not hold back their urine and when, in a corner, a lost woman in the midst of this pitiful herd wept noiselessly from closed eyes.

Towards the end of July the heat chased Rose and her companion from their favourite place against the wall. Mrs Mingot had stood it as long as she could: she was afraid that Rose might escape her somewhere else. . . . For hours she would watch her weep, not without some pleasure, finding in her tears unreserved approval, a justification of her theories of hopelessness and hell. Nevertheless she decided to look for a little shade. 'If we stay here, you'll turn into a "Section Three",' she said to Rose. 'They'd separate us. . . .'

They went over and sat in the middle of the lawn, among the other women who, for the last few days, had been crossing beyond the syringa bushes. But in this newly conquered space the asylum community caught up with them again, noisier and more disorderly than ever. From time to time Roubillot screamed, as she did in the dormitory: her peacock's cry, a break in the silent massacre which raged in her heart day and night. The dark-haired woman whom they called Redempcion somersaulted over the heads of the others and then collapsed on the grass, showing her thighs, eyes closed in a sort of ambiguous dizziness. Gertrude crawled across the lawn. Others sang, with a blade of grass ringed round a finger; the world was immense between the syringa bushes. Suddenly it was the slope of a hill, where grass brides screeched out a chorale in falsetto voices; it was the heart of a black forest where Roubillot screamed. An odour of baked laurels hung in the air. Lying on her back, her eyes closed and her arms stretched out palms down against the ground, Rose felt the summer earth, the great luminous day ripple away from her to blurred horizons. Her white smock dazzling in the sunlight, a nurse came across the lawn and clapped her hands.

'Ah, that's right, visitors' day today,' said Mrs Mingot and hurriedly helped Rose to her feet. 'When it's too hot, they don't use the parlour; they come out here on the grass, and we get locked in. . . .'

At the door, several women were pleading with the nurse. They never had any visitors and they wanted to bring chairs down from the dormitory as the visitors would need them. It was a job worth fighting for. The men spoke words different from those here. The women wore print dresses. Freedom gave them all the elegance and grace of riches.

'I don't want to see them, you know,' said Mrs Mingot to Rose when they had come into the hall, 'I know only too well what illusions they represent and what treason they bring with them. Don't leave me, Rose! I haven't told you the end of my story with the Hungarians yet, you know, the story I was telling you this morning. Come over here, close to me. . . . What are you looking at over there, Rose?'

The other women seemed more nervous, too. The heat made them tense. During the last several days, whenever they clustered together, madness took over: not noisily, but insidiously, crawling like vermin that they might have been passing from one to the other.

'I have the feeling that she'll come today,' said a young woman next to Louise.

There were so many freckles on her face, so much hope, that Rose and several other women turned to look at her.

'Yes, certainly my mother is coming!' repeated the young woman with an air of ecstasy. Mrs Mingot shrugged. 'Your mother! How do you know? I'm asking you: what do you know about it? And even if she did come: Here, my child, I've brought you chocolate and some hard-boiled eggs, a real travel basket. It is a long trip, I know, my child, I know, but we must be patient. Patience! Tastes like sand. Here you are in the middle of the desert, and they tell you: "Eat some sand!" '

Outside, the gravel was crunching under the feet of the first visitors. 'Don't listen to her!' a white-haired inmate shouted to the young woman. 'I'm sure she'll come. I'll let you know when

I hear her step. I can always tell their step when they're old like I am. Don't worry. I'm listening. . . . '

She hid her face in her hands, while the young woman remained wide-eyed before her hope, which was going to sink, she could feel it, and already she was swallowing her tears.

The nurse opened the door, called a name, and the chosen woman stood up and walked towards her with the exalted expression of someone who has rediscovered her secret. Mrs Mingot had fallen asleep. Rose went over to the window and stood behind the women who were gathered there, watching. Perhaps he would come today?

A man dressed in black passed right in front of their faces, saw them, bowed furtively and hurried towards the lawn. Then came two fat women, carrying black oilcloth shopping bags. They were red and sweaty. Here, everyone was pale; one never perspired. Little Treguel stuck her tongue out at them and they walked off. The nurse kept opening and closing the door.

'Blanche Premontier! Adéle Caillon! Julia Vuillaume! Martha Benoux!'

The woman advanced; most often silent, she submitted to effusive greetings, with her arms limp at her sides and, after the visitor had sat down, she, too, sat down on one of the iron chairs her companions had eagerly brought.

To escape the silence and the embarrassment, packages were hastily taken out of linen bags, out of old leather briefcases, and unwrapped; in this silence of surprise and mutual affliction, one clutched at the helpfulness, the humble eloquence of these primitive offerings. Then the eating began, often shared with a good will bordering on disgust by the visitor who tried to put the madwoman at ease, to let her bask in the warmth of complicity. Then, eagerly peeling an orange for her: 'I think we're in luck, they seem to be nice and juicy,' he began a conversation.

From the window Rose and her companions caught snatches of sentences, torn from a long and colourless family chronicle.

'Ernestine is expecting a baby, in January, probably. . . .'

He stretched his news with brief comments, marked by a sort of serene resignation. 'Ah yes, life goes fast!' he nodded and quickly out of the corner of his eye, treacherously, he spied on the patient's reactions. What sort of trap was this?

'But . . . you remember Ernestine, your cousin who married a Gillet,' the messenger repeated softly, discouraged by his wife's silence. 'The one who lives near the post office, next to the drugstore. . . .'

And little by little he got caught in the absurd universe of Ernestine whom his insistence was giving new dimensions.

'So you're still in love with her?'

He restrained himself.

'What are you talking about? Please, Camilla, pay a little attention to your words. You know very well that Ernestine . . .'

Ernestine again. He couldn't get out of it. He would leave here, stamped with Ernestine. The trap he had laid was closing in on him. Close your eyes, the story flows like an undammed stream. . . .

'Is she crying?' asked a woman nearby.

'No, Ma'am, she is pretending to be asleep,' answered the man wearily. 'She used to do that even before she fell ill. It's as though one weren't there, as though one didn't exist.'

He shook his head, wrapped up his gifts and placed them on the knees of the pretending sleeper. 'There is no Ernestine in my life. . . .'

Many inmates remained fiercely silent in the presence of their visitors. Their mouths became powdered with flour as they bit into a cake, held in both hands, with the same voracity with which, the rest of the time, they threw themselves upon certain words, upon certain images, since they no longer belonged to a world fed on reason. The visitors looked at them, smiling at first, but soon, as the woman stuffed larger and larger pieces into her mouth, their approval stretched to a look of worried surprise. Anyone else would have choked, but no, she looked at them, calmly, her throat bloated like a goitre. Don't worry! She would never swallow anything so big, so round as her suffering. . . .

When she had finished, they tilted back their iron chairs, let their eyes wander about with casual interest: they were taking in the facts. After having seemed oppressive for a long time, the asylum had become an excursion similar to those on which, during their vacations, they went to visit 'curiosities of nature', rocks pierced by cascades, blue-walled grottoes, menhirs where the wind moans like an animal: here, the creations of insanity were offered to their sight, it was, they felt, a little more interesting than intertwining trees. Standing with two feet planted squarely on the shore, they watched the waves foam at the edge of the sea where it bordered on the shifting sands. . . .

Listlessly Rose listened to their conversations; mechanically, she observed their secret movements.

Mrs Mingot's words came back to her: these people were perhaps in reality nothing but phantoms of memory, persons born of regret to give this simulacrum of life. When you examined them closely, their very naturalness betrayed them. At certain moments they really overdid it.

What a bad actor Ernestine's false lover was: he had placed oranges in his wife's lap. Her eyes were still closed, and every time she seemed about to move or breathed a little more heavily, he hastily put his hand on the oranges to keep them from rolling to the ground. When equilibrium returned – had it been disturbed at all? – he withdrew his hand with extreme slowness, a lingering caress.

An even worse actress was the fat woman in the black spangled dress who was sitting with a girl with a ribbon in her hair. She was blowing into a small goldbeater's skin with a sort of whistle valve. As the balloon grew fatter, clearer and more transparent, the cheeks of the fat woman, distended with effort, paled and bulged. At last she pulled the valve out of her mouth and, letting the balloon empty itself with a sort of monotoned meow, she looked at her daughter with moist eyes and smiled.

It was what one calls 'a pitiful smile' and that wasn't any more acceptable, that fat woman holding this collapsed, wrinkled piece of skin in her fingers, and who was going to start all over again because probably a light had come into her daughter's eyes and who, for a change of taste, would finally pull some gingerbread men out of a brown paper bag. Her daughter was at least twenty.

And the indifferent ones, the architects who were endlessly measuring the asylum buildings with their eyes, allowing themselves to admit once again with visible satisfaction that we did not want for anything, all the stones were neatly in their places, and plentiful, one had to admit, the city did not stint when it came to stones. Play acting, all of it.

'He is waiting for me somewhere else,' thought Rose, 'he is real, but how can I call him, hear his answer, direct myself towards him, join him?'

The visiting hour was almost over. The visitors left and waved their hands over their heads, sometimes even without turning back.

'Well, what has this performance taught you?' asked Mrs Mingot dryly, taking Rose's arm. 'He didn't come, obviously. and you didn't recognize anybody in this make-believe crowd, They have all been carefully screened, believe me, not one of them could bring you the slightest help.'

The doors of the big hall were pushed open again; they went out into the yard. The women had not yet taken up their places on the lawn. They were standing in groups, or alone, depending on whether the event had raised their hopes or shattered them.

'Well, what did I tell you!' said Mrs Mingot to the young woman with freckles. 'She didn't come, huh?'

The young woman was standing at the door; her eyes were red; she did not seem to hear. Mrs Mingot left her to her dreaming and pulled Rose away. 'See what a bad habit hope is. . . .'

Near them, Gertrude who had had a visit, was talking loudly

to a circle of women: 'They swore that it was so. Five hundred yards from here, and you know what they said: "It should have been put further away." They thought I hadn't heard it. I asked them: "And why should it have been put further away?" They looked at each other, and the fat one who always talks answered: "Well, because it is a fair . . .!"'

'He promised me, oh I don't know what you call it, what do you call it, something absolutely marvellous,' said a woman with real tears of joy in her eyes. 'God knows, he must have worked day and night to buy it for me. "You'll have it, you'll have it," he kept saying, "you'll have it, you'll have it. . . ."'

They laughed and laughed, biting on their hands, stamping their feet, and the woman with the present raised her brimming eyes towards the sky where her joy continued to exist.

Towards evening the agitation died down; copper-coloured clouds had climbed the sky. Nurses could be heard calling the time to each other across the sections: 'Twenty to!' A white smock disappeared behind black leaves. Evening: would hope ever be born again? A little later, after they had gone to bed, the sounds of a country fair came over the trees and the asylum walls.

'Hear that? Hear that? What did I tell you!' cried Gertrude, sitting up in bed.

The stalls of the fair had been thrown up at a certain distance from the asylum gates. Only a vague, oozing music filtered through, punctuated by metallic sounds from the shooting galleries. In the windows the iron bars and the leaves stood out against a sky that was hardly any paler than usual.

'I'm going!' Gertrude declared loudly, encouraged by the total absence of nurses; they were probably watching the fair from the attic windows. 'Yes, as you see me standing here, I'm going to take a look at the fair. After all, the fair is for everybody!' she exclaimed fiercely, as though sensing objections in the shadows. 'Once I saw an ex-convict at a fair. They brought him the ducks they had won at the shooting stands and whack!

he'd cut their heads off. You should have seen him! No one dared make a move. The fair isn't France, you know!'

'Yeah, she'll try it all right. I'm sure the guards have guns. . . .' It was Mrs Mingot's voice.

'Shit guns!' cried Gertrude.

She bounced out of bed and started to dress.

'What's she doing?' came a worried voice from the other end of the dormitory.

'What's she doing?' asked a woman without lifting her head in a voice of great sickness. 'My God, why did they put out my eyes?'

'And the wall?' said somone. 'How will you get across the wall?'

Gertrude explained that she had a long, heavy nail, which she had stolen from the masons some weeks ago, and that she would stick it in between two bricks to give herself a grip and hoist herself to the top.

'She has a nail,' reported the echo, 'she has a nail as big as a dagger. . . .'

'A dagger,' affirmed the echo, returning from the other end of the dormitory.

Near Rose, in the aisle which separated the two beds, Gertrude finished getting dressed. One could hear her whistling breath. Meanwhile, around her, the excitement reached a peak; faced with the gravity of the event, each woman rediscovered a little of her sanity.

Finally Gertrude left the dormitory. She was walking on tiptoe, a finger on her lips: she had forgotten to tie the belt of her asylum dress. Mrs Mingot pointed it out with a ferocious little laugh, and by this detail alone one felt that Gertrude was lost. In the distance the fair was probably going strong. The noise had grown louder. But perhaps it was only an approaching storm: one must watch out for everything in this world.

Women got up to go to the toilets, dawdled in the dormitory, kept swinging the hall doors. Mrs Mingot came over to Rose's bed.

'I'm afraid for you, you are in the next bed. They'll question you, grill you. God, what a dreadful night!'

She squeezed Rose's arm through the covers and headed towards the hall door.

In the dormitory the women continued to talk about the fair:

'That's what happens at fairs,' said a voice lost in darkness. 'I had never trusted those dark alleys between the wagons; and the little gypsy girl who was doing the split, do you imagine he didn't look at her. I was only good enough for slapping, and when he went over to the shooting gallery with some two hundred people around it, I stood there like a fool watching him aim at a red tin pigeon, and what did I suddenly understand: he was aiming at my hand! I was wearing red gloves that day, he was aiming at my hand, at my hand. . . .'

'Come, Bertha, you're exaggerating! Go to sleep. . . .'

'What a silly idea to have taken him to the fair. A man just moves a finger, and everything goes. . . .'

'My hand,' the woman whined once more, mechanically, hardly believing it herself. Then, one after the other, they fell silent, carried away by the merry-go-round, their own silent merry-go-round to which they clung each night.

Quite a long time had gone by when a nurse came into the dormitory and snapped on all the lights.

Soon afterwards Gertrude appeared, held between two other nurses. Strands of wet hair hung down either side of her thin face. She was wrapped in a sheet down to her ankles, walking barefoot with quick, short steps.

She was crying, her chin on her chest; every sob made her shoulders heave; when she reached her bed the nurses took the sheet off and dressed her in a shirt. The skin of her body was whipped red from the shower, from wet towels thrown with washerwoman energy. She was still breathless. The nurses put her to bed, lifting her up by her feet and under the arms: they put her in the grave.

The nurses went out chatting. The last one slammed the

door of the partition which separated them from the dormitory and soon all the lights went out; sounds from the fair could still be heard. Later everything fell silent and it rained. Rose sat up then and edged her hand towards Gertrude's bed. She was still crying and so deeply lost in her torment that the presence of this hand did not surprise her, if she sensed it at all. At this point, anything might help. Rose moved her hand towards Gertrude's forehead. Sitting up suddenly, Gertrude bit her.

The incidents of that night left hardly any traces. The next morning very few women seemed to remember. Half aloud, they accused Mrs Mingot of having squealed on Gertrude. A pointless accusation: Gertrude was not sent to Section Three; nor was she disciplined, or even questioned, and what's more, she, herself, didn't seem in any way surprised at this. It was understood that here life was erased, memory abandoned. Only Mrs Mingot tried to revive the incident. The noises of the fair were gone. It was a weekday, at noon.

'You see how powerful they are,' Mrs Mingot said to Louise. 'They made a whole fair move away. And to think some people still go around imagining that they have rights! That they'll leave here, one day, that they'll escape the regulations! No, no, Rose, we are their creatures and the world belongs to them. They conjure up visits for us, and the sounds of a fair, and then they erase it all. The strategy of bait, and that's what you call life. You don't realize how happy they are to hear you say that word. That's all they want. . . .'

But Rose said nothing. She was lying flat on her back in the grass. She was thinking of Paul. How he loved her! She would like to prove it to all these doubters. . . .

'Wake up, Rose,' said Mrs Mingot, 'here they come. Sit up! Sit up; don't make a spectacle of yourself.'

Rose sat up and looked about her, scattering a handful of grass.

'They're heading straight for us,' said Mrs Mingot. 'You're

the one they have it in for. I'll leave you. But please, my dear, defend yourself. Don't let them take you away, Rose. Promise me, promise your old friend.'

She scuttled off, her shoulders hunched. The men were coming closer. Rose recognized their grave faces because, from time to time, these men came wandering through the section to question some of the women. They all talked at the same time, without raising their voices, then fell silent and took notes on a pad.

'Who are you?' a woman asked them, desperate with daring.

'Who are we?' answered one of them. 'But you know very well, we are the people who are going to let you go home very soon, if you are reasonable and obedient. . . .'

'Oh, but I am obedient!' cried the woman, full of sudden hope. 'Ask the head nurse! She thinks I'm the best one here!'

The four men continued their walk, stopping when their conversation became animated, walking on again, deep in thought, tormented by the objections they would soon have to express, with a frown and a crooked forefinger rubbing the side of their noses. But the woman did not let them get away; she trailed them, her face tense, her mouth spewing formulas of servility, obsequious words, denunciation. Another minute and she would be on her knees.

A nurse finally decided to intervene and, caught in the game of obedience, the woman let herself be led away without protest; this was the final test, of course. They were watching her obey. It was only when she arrived in the hall and the door closed behind her that she understood that they had tricked her, that they were not going to call her back and grant her their nod of approval. She pressed her cheeks against the greenish windowpane and watched them walk away, her face drowned in childhood grief.

They stopped near Rose who remained seated on the grass.

'I remember her,' one of them said. 'I saw her when she was admitted. Nothing terrible, it seems.'

'No, just a confused state, overstrain plus a sentimental

trauma,' replied a man with a white crew cut. 'We have left her alone and she is slowly coming out of it by herself. Perhaps the real problem is going to start now. . . .'

'Don't talk to me about those problems,' sighed one of the two men who had been silent until now. 'They give me more trouble than anything that happens before. I am supposed to cure human beings. But three times out of four I am helpless. I'd have to cure their lives as well!'

'Yes, it is my impression that, in her case, the second part of the programme is the most important,' the white-haired man said again.

'Where is Paul, my husband?' asked Rose, getting up.

She was talking to the man who had spoken last, and not without a certain intention of violence but, finding his eyes and seeing the sympathy in them, she felt lost and started to tie and untie the ends of her belt in front of her dress.

'Your husband,' replied the man, studying his nails, 'your husband. . . .' His hand no longer interested him and his eyes returned to Rose's face. 'I'll soon find out where he is and I'll let you know, yes,' he continued with suspect cordiality, 'one of these days the two of us must have a nice little chat. I'll send for you.'

Since the beginning of this exchange one of the men had been watching the speaker with a questioning look. He noticed it as he turned away from Rose. He made a face. Rose saw it. It was the sort of face a doctor makes on his way out of the sickroom to say that things are serious or, at least, not too good.

'It's banal and complicated all at once,' he murmured, 'a broken marriage, he left her; it happens every day, but the unusual part is her refusal . . .'

He walked on and continued to talk to the others. 'Obviously he can't ask for a divorce as long as she's in here!' he exclaimed at one point. 'But that's probably the least of his worries. . . .'

Suddenly he feared that he had spoken too loudly and turned back to see whether Rose had overheard. She was staring at him, wide-eyed. That's when he noticed her wounded hand.

'What happened?' he asked, going up to Rose. 'What happened to your hand?'

'Gertrude bit me,' replied Rose and began to suck her wound.

'I can see you smiling, yes, I can see you smiling, my dear President,' said the man with the white crew cut, turning towards one of his companions. 'You are probably thinking of what I said a moment ago: that the asylum cures. And in your mind you answer: yes, but this woman is desperate because she doesn't see her husband; locked inside these walls she goes up to Gertrude, and Gertrude bites her. And I'll throw more oil on your fire: Do you know what happened last night to Gertrude? She tried to escape and they caught her. I might add that, in these cases, the nurses are rather firm. And so you say: how can the asylum cure anybody? It's a hell. . . ."

'It is you who are using the word "hell", not I. I wouldn't go quite so far,' answered the man they called President.

'Well, I authorize you to go that far,' said the other. 'Let's assume that this is hell: sometimes there is no screaming – although not always – no frenzy and of course no torture. It may seem lukewarm, vague, dull, but hell burns with a low flame like those apartment heaters that you can touch without burning your hand, but they're suffocating. In short, this is a prison, a place of punishment – a hell, to use that word again. And this atmosphere of punishment imposes itself.

'The best would be, of course, if each one of these women, surprised by the onslaught of fate, recognized the need to hold court in herself. How much time we would save! She would soon discover that the hell is inside, that there exists, within her, far away, a state of grace, a deserted paradise. Please note the word "deserted". Insanity is often an evasion, a desertion, thus, very often related to guilt. Note that, when I speak of hell, I refer to this young woman in particular. As long as she refuses to accept the truth, her truth. . . . But I want her to find it by herself. . . . Yes, I assure you! She knows it perfectly!' he exclaimed, in answer to one of the other men's questions.

He stepped aside, getting out of Rose's way. She ran off.

Hell! Out of reach, she slowed down and wandered about the sunny courtyard which was treacherous, too, like the rest of the world, a crossroads for innumerable evils.

Someone touched her arm.

'Ah, Mrs Mingot!' said Rose, clutching her companion's shoulder.

'What did they say to you? What did they do to you?' asked Mrs Mingot with a sort of radiant pity.

'We're in hell,' said Rose, with a frown, as though this word had been hiding a problem.

'Aha! In hell! Why yes, indeed! A fine discovery you've made there, my dear girl!' replied Mrs Mingot. 'Your old friend has been telling you that every day, but you didn't believe her. Others have to come and break the big news: we're in hell!'

'No, no, he didn't want that,' murmured Rose to herself. 'Hell doesn't exist. Not for me! Not for me!'

'What are you saying, Rose? I don't understand,' said Mrs Mingot.

Rose looked through her: her eyes were wide open – on her memories.

'Come, I'll tell you, I'll prove it to you!' she cried after a moment, pulling Mrs Mingot after her with sudden authority.

The sun was dropping. They went to sit in their regular place against the wall. For a moment Rose kept her face in her hands, then she raised her head. Her eyes fixed a distant point in space, like people who perfectly remember a certain date but seem to go on looking for it way back in their memory, because they want to measure the road they've travelled since then.

Finally she named the year and the season of that year when her story began, and she began to talk. She was going to talk for a long, a very long time. For whole days, whole weeks, for months. She was going to talk in the morning, while waiting for day to come into the dining room, waiting among her companions half awake in their insanity, sitting fearfully, pressed one against the other on the benches. She was going to talk in the boredom of the autumn days, when it is only five o'clock and the rain beats against the foggy windows. She was going to talk at night, at the metal-covered table that offered an endless succession of boneless meals, grey gruels, lukewarm soups, tasteless food that seemed to be prechewed. And she was going to talk on their way to the dormitory, before she pulled the rough, formaldehyde-scented sheets over her forgotten body. And even then her monologue would only seem to stop. Eyes closed, on the edge of sleep, she went over and over the events of her life. It was not simple reverie, an easy stream of images. Her memories were arranged in the order of a legal claim: through them ran the thread of her defence.

In her confidences to Mrs Mingot, Rose dwelled upon unimportant incidents, all of which belonged to the beginning of her married idyll. She obviously felt little desire to risk herself beyond that. Perhaps her memory simply did not go any further? Now that she had rediscovered this memory, how precisely, how frantically she re-created this happy phase of her past! Details abounded. A door was opened. A door was closed. One day they had lost a key. . . . Mrs Mingot held up her hand and nodded: no need to go any further. She was already well enough informed.

'That was a warning, my dear,' she declared. 'And it was unforgivable of you not to have understood.'

'But what was there to understand?' asked Rose.

She plunged her face between her hands. Her thoughts were wandering. And then, winter was interfering now. Winter was a terribly mental season here, because then insanity was cloistered. Parked in the half-light of the room, largely deprived of movement, the women passionately played with signs and superstitions.

This was probably due to the influence of several merchants of the supernatural, palm readers and clairvoyants whom an excess of spiritual effort and exploration of the beyond had led to the asylum where they continued to practise their obscure religion. They had quickly made disciples, because there was hardly a patient who did not feel the need to hold some identifiable power responsible for her visions and 'voices', to give her delirium a place in a superior, well-ordered hierarchy.

Occultism was less an aggregate of beliefs than an enterprise of justification. It was good to know that tables turned under the hands of spiritualists, because it explained once and for all any form of dizziness one might experience. Magic legitimized the instability of objects, the birth of phantoms, the persecutions of invisible, hollow-voiced prosecutors. Dog-eared, greasy tarot decks passed from hand to hand:

'Well, dearie, shall I do a full reading for you?' asked a fat woman dressed in blue cloth, taking a seat at the table across from a quiet young girl who had arrived only recently.

The muteness of the newcomers, still paralysed with fear, the sort of dull stupor they had kept when they left life, always attracted the fat mammas whose eyes, after several years in the asylum, shone again with a malicious light, almost a glimmer of sanity. The girl stared straight ahead, her hand smoothing out the greasy metal table top in front of her.

'Let's go; hands off now and cut!' the fat mama ordered gently, smoothing her cards. 'Nothing more reliable. . . .'

Several women came wandering over.

'Come on, let's take a look,' said Mrs Mingot, getting up. Since Rose had begun to talk, Mrs Mingot had become more turbulent, more interested in the community life. Since she no longer had 'the floor', she was looking for other distractions.

Rose's monologue had been interrupted. She didn't want to move. She let her old friend go and leaned her head against the glossy wall, a welcome respite that permitted her to go back over the points of her defence and verify them one by one with a detachment which the speed and the unexpected dovetailing of facts did not always permit while she was 'telling herself' to Mrs Mingot. Who could deny it? Our understanding was deep and complete. One rarely sees a couple as united as we were . . . as we still are. No matter what they do, we are still those two united beings. . . .

She was going to cry again, she was already crying while laughter burst out at the table where ten women were now leaning over the fortune teller.

'A blond young man! Did you hear that? The cards predict the visit of a blond young man. We'll know all about it!' they shouted round the girl who was paying no attention to her own destiny.

'A little quiet please, ladies!' ordered Big Mama Houdin.

They calmed down. There was only the clicking noise of Mama Houdin's forefinger, jumping from card to card.

'One, two, three, four: Death! One, two, three, four: Death!' a skinny, white-haired woman began to chant, rising suddenly to her full height. She left the table, beating time with her hands.

Voices rose up behind her: 'Hey you! Shut up!'

Once more all heads bent over the cards. But the signal had been given. Already everything was echoing the incantation that continued, all the way down at the other end of the dining hall, where the white-haired woman paced back and forth, clapping her hands.

'Spades again!'

There was the ace of spades, a black heart on a stem. They stared at the girl with sharp curiosity.

'You're going to die, do you hear!' cried Redempcion, shaking the girl as one shakes a sleeper. 'Are you deaf? Show your palm! She's going to die, huh?'

Puffed up with glory, her face shiny with satisfaction and sweat, Big Mama Houdin nodded her head in agreement without even bothering to read the girl's palm which Redempcion was holding out to her. Slowly she gathered up the cards, without paying any more attention to the girl who was looking at her with eyes already full of tears, and wringing her hands.

'She's speechless, imagine what a shock!' said the women, examining her very closely, and still more closely, fixedly, ready to touch her porcelain cheek with their fingers.

The hubbub pulled Rose out of her thoughts. 'Who is she? What's her name?' she asked Mrs Mingot who was coming back with an excited, radiant face. 'I don't think I know her.'

'Iphigenia. She arrived two days ago. You know, Houdin dealt her cards very carefully, conscientiously. She even seemed inspired for once. Of course you never can tell with these fat people, still, the evidence is there: it seems that the girl is going to die. . . .'

The girl had got up and was spinning round under the unbearable stares of the madwomen. She had been condemned unanimously, and Rose, who saw nothing but a cruel game in this verdict, an absurd ritual, supported the sentence by her immobility, by her indifference. Besides, she no longer felt any pity. She would do nothing to console the unfortunate young woman who was wandering about the room in the greyish light. Her own past was still devoured by night; it needed all her attention, and besides, a sort of physical repulsion excluded her a little more each day from those whose fate she shared.

Their physical degradation hindered contact even more than their unbalanced minds. Insanity soured their breath, left a slight odour of urine and sweat in their clothes, swelled their breasts with ridiculous ardour, moistened their lips with constant drooling, spoiled all sexuality and in voluminous, shaggy dresses, their bottoms looked like little overstuffed chairs.

'You see, my dear. . . .' said Mrs Mingot.

But Redempcion had come up to them. 'Do you know the prayers for the dead?' she asked Rose.

Rose shrugged her shoulders. She was not religious.

But nevertheless she dreamily repeated Redempcion's words: 'The prayers for the dead. . . .'

They were the kind of words that suddenly uncover the sea. the black night; the wind beating the water like a curtain.

'I know them!' replied Mrs Mingot. 'I've sat through

enough wakes, during the war! We commend to Thee, O Lord, the soul of Thy handmaid, dead to this world, may she live only for Thee and may Thy infinite compassion wipe away . . .'

'Okay,' said Redempcion, her voice suddenly grave. 'It's for the new girl. Houdin said so. She doesn't have much more time. We've made her sit down. We're not going to let her die like a dog!' she yelled, clenching her fists. 'Who knows, maybe tomorrow they'll take her away, all stiff and dead and shove her into the morgue without a drop of holy water. You believe in God. Well, let me tell you, so do I. I, too, am the soul of Thy handmaid, come on, let's get going. . . .'

Mrs Mingot hesitated.

'After all, I do have the right,' she said to Rose, trying to convince herself. 'I represent the Red Cross, as far as I know. . . .'

She got up and followed Redempcion.

The girl was sitting at the other end of the room, guarded by three women like a prisoner awaiting execution.

'What's the use of looking?' Rose said to herself. Anything that did not concern her history left her unmoved. She tried to convince herself. And yet, there were moments. . . . Again she let her head fall back against the glossy wall. But soon voices rose at the other end of the room, voices she did not recognize. She opened her eyes. The girl was sitting on a bench. She was absolutely immobile. Four women were kneeling at her feet.

'Let's start again,' said one of them, turning to the others.

It was Mrs Mingot. Rose noticed that a black wool shawl had been thrown over the girl's head, half covering her face. Suddenly she was fascinated by the spectacle. The four women took up the chorus again, with shaky voices.

'By Thy Precious Blood, have mercy on Thy faithful trespassers.

'Poor sinners we are, beseeching Thy Mercy.'

'Thy Mercy!' shouted Mrs Mingot, trying to cover the stammering of the others.

'Thy Mer-cy!' declaimed Mrs Mingot.

'Close your eyes,' Rose told herself, suddenly overcome by a nameless distress.

'We beseech Thee therefore that Thy Judicial Sentence weigh not heavily upon her,' chanted the unrelenting voices.

'Together! Together!' ordered someone.

"Aren't they ever going to finish?' thought Rose, struggling to keep her eyes closed.

'We beseech Thee therefore that Thy Judicial Sentence weigh not heavily upon her!' chanted the voices, suddenly joined by many others. 'That Thy Judicial Sentence weigh not heavily upon her!' The clamour increased.

'You must open your eyes,' Rose told herself. A hand was touching her shoulder, shaking her. She found herself standing behind the woman who had roused her from her feigned nap. 'Do Thou conduct her to a place of peace and rest!'

All the women, some standing, some kneeling on the tiles, turned towards the seated girl whose face was now completely covered by the black veil.

'Together!' someone shouted again.

The noise swelled like a coming storm.

'Do Thou, O Lord, rescue this soul from the flame and may the angels lead her to the land of the living,' the women repeated after Mrs Mingot. 'To the land of the living. Lamb of God Who takest away the sins of the world, grant her eternal peace. Eternal peace!' the women repeated in chorus. Some were crying; one could hear tears under their voices; others, on their knees, were clutching the benches, their heads bent back.

'Lamb of God,' implored a voice a little further away and borne upon the resonance of the room, 'grant her eternal peace!'

'What if he is dead!' Rose thought all of a sudden.

Her hands began to tremble, her whole body trembled. 'No, that's impossible! Lamb of God, deliver me from this thought! Lamb of God!' she was going to shout herself when, suddenly, everything fell silent. The prayer was probably over, it had always been like that in her life. . . .

Mrs Mingot found Rose prostrate on the bench and thought that she was sleeping. Attracted by the noise, nurses paced up and down the room, doing surprise about-faces with angry looks. They had taken the shawl off the girl's head. She continued to stare straight ahead, without moving.

'No matter what they do, she's had the last rites,' said Mrs Mingot.

Her face glowed with contentment and she looked with tenderness at Rose who had just opened her eyes.

'I've had a ghastly thought,' murmured Rose, 'something like a revelation. But it's not true! It can't be true!' she cried, shaking her head, plunging her face into her hands.

'Then why talk about it, if it isn't true?' replied Mrs Mingot. 'These truths are quite enough for the time being,' she added, pointing to the girl for whom she had prayed. She sighed. 'Ah, I don't like to see death come back among us. You'll see: one death always brings another. This one will start a whole series. . . . A year or so ago, it began with Lydia, a Czech. For several days we had all noticed that she was growing taller. Not much, just enough for me to know what it was all about: death often comes on tiptoe. Days passed; it was in the month of March, if I remember correctly, there were daffodils in the garden: I detest daffodils. One night Lydia went up to bed, straight as an "I". She had the bed at my right. Suddenly, in the middle of the night, I saw her pale white hand flutter like a bird's wing. I yelled: "The dove! The dove!" Everybody thought I was dreaming. At that time everybody yelled at night in the dormitory. Not like now. We put up a good fight . . . well, anyhow, the next morning Lydia was dead, dead. . . . Let me finish!' shouted Mrs Mingot who thought that Rose, who had begun to fidget, wanted to interrupt her.

'Dead?' said Rose pensively.

Without hearing her, her friend went right on.

'After Lydia, two other women died in the same fashion. Lydia had thrown them the line on her way out. . . . Why did they die? Why? For the salvation of their country, for the revolution? To protest to the face of heaven? To redeem our sins? Yes, perhaps for this, perhaps for that. Yes, perhaps for this and for that together. But dead all the same, Rose! Dead, I tell you!

'No cause, no salvation stands up to this total blackness. Death denies everything. Every night I could argue that day never existed: the sky would prove me right. Death is really the worst catastrophe: everything collapses with you. Love never existed; light never existed. Everything negated in an instant. All those crumpled images, those feelings, every second of life, the sun: I used to exist. Nothing replaces existence. They were as dead as a handful of pebbles, condemned by death, betrayed by death, they were wearing the stone hat, Rose, the stone hat!'

She buried her face in her hands and Rose respected her silence. 'Why is she telling me all this? Does she know something?'

'What about him, do you think he is dead?' she finally asked the old woman in a trembling voice.

Mrs Mingot looked up. Her face was dry, her eyes were calm.

'But this has nothing to do with him, Rose, why should this have anything to do with him? I am only thinking of us, we're the only ones who count now. You are here, you are with us, my dear! Warm and cuddly and for a good long time. Leave that man in peace, he is resting far, far away, a little farther every day. You are no longer his life. You are no longer in his life. He is no longer in yours. Isn't everything just right that way? Only one thing: not to die, no, not to die just yet. . . .'

Nervously she clutched at Rose's hand as though, in saying these words, she were facing a danger. Rose pulled her hand away sharply.

'What does death matter to me, if he is dead, or if I am never to see him again!' she cried.

Mrs Mingot shrugged and got up. Some of the women were

gathering again at the other end of the room where the girl for whom they had prayed was sitting. Mrs Mingot went over to find out how things stood. Rose was escaping her a little more every day. She had to do something to console herself.

The old woman's words had not frightened Rose. She did not believe in these fables, but that such superstitions (Paul's intentional staying away, his indifference) were at all possible, threw her into a kind of fit. So they had come to think, around here, that from the depth of his silence Paul approved of the punishment that was being inflicted upon her, that he was trying to make it even harder. What nonsense! Still, for over two months she had been almost entirely sane again, lucid, yet she was still as locked up, as abandoned as on the first day. The doctor who had, one day, talked of hell in front of her, often walked through Section Two: 'Rose Schmidt, you'll be angry with me again!' he exclaimed as soon as he saw her. 'I still have not received any information concerning your husband. No, you needn't tell me that I should write, I have already written several times. But we ought to have a little chat, one of these days, you and I. But not just yet, my dear, not just yet. I'm much too busy. And besides, we still have a little more progress to make before we are completely well again. Come now, it's not so bad here, is it: the food has been much, much better during the last month, hasn't it? And the room is nice and warm now. If all goes well, I'll have some raffia brought in in a couple of days. Did you hear that, little Mother Lormot? And you, Redempcion, listen to this: next week I'll have bundles of raffia and cane brought in here, and a few tools which we'll entrust to the most reasonable, and a few pots of paint as well. To begin we'll have someone teach you how to braid baskets and sandals and sun hats. . . .'

'Sun hats!' exclaimed Mother Lormot with a shrug, pointing to the window. The sky was low. Fog drifted in the black branches. As a consolation one could always tell oneself that it was going to snow. But sun hats! There would never be any sun again. Two months ago it had rolled behind the trees like a severed head and no one had spoke of it since.

'But these hats won't be for you,' replied the man. 'We'll sell them. It will bring in money for you all.'

'Could we braid them in different designs in different colours?' asked Gertrude.

'Certainly!' cried the stout man with enthusiasm. 'We're not opposed to imagination. I just told you, I'll bring you paints. Those with a feeling for art can create to their heart's content.'

'Perhaps we could also make little mats,' timidly suggested a young girl at Big Mama Houdin's arm. She had ribbons in her hair like a schoolgirl.

'A good idea; a splendid idea!' cried the man. 'Little mats to place under a plate, or for serving tea. Oh, I can see that you have lots of ideas. I'll soon have a workshop buzzing with champion straw weavers. . . . Only Rose Schmidt isn't saying anything. . . .'

'She is thinking about her husband,' said Mrs Mingot flatly. 'Why don't you tell her the truth? She is strong enough to take it. And besides, I'm here. At least let her hate him, once and for all!'

The stout man flushed purple. 'It's none of your business!' he screamed. 'I wasn't talking to you! Mrs Mingot, I'm fully aware that you never miss an opportunity to talk all kinds of rubbish, always trying to make things worse, and your condition has nothing to do with it. I know you, and I give you one last warning: change your behaviour, or else. . . .'

Mrs Mingot showed the first signs of panic which she always felt when she was directly confronted, but this time the affront was in public, and her pride carried her away. 'Change my behaviour?' she asked with feigned surprise. 'Annette, go and fetch me another behaviour, please,' she said, lifting the hem of her asylum dress between two fingers and pointing at it with her chin.

Several women burst out laughing. The stout man stared at

her with blazing eyes. 'And you over there, with nothing to do but fold your arms,' pursued Mrs Mingot, encouraged by her success, 'didn't you hear: I absolutely must, I have been commanded, to change "behaviour", and I need space for my further evolutions. These walls are much too close together. Knock them down for me, will you! Or else our dear director will have a fit. . . .'

'Mrs Mingot, that's enough of your act!' shouted the stout man, taking a step towards the old woman. 'Get out of here! Go into the yard, that's an order! Mrs Lemercier!' he called, turning about.

Alerted by the loud voices, the nurse came running at once. The scene had excited the women. They were drifting into disorder. They snickered at Mrs Mingot's last words, they laughed and forgot to stop laughing; there was something mechanical, suddenly painful in their throats. 'Hand over your keys then, if you want me to go out!' shrieked Mrs Mingot, now completely out of control. 'We don't get to see your keys very often, Mr Behaviour Changer, they're always snuggling in your pocket, those darling keys! We can wait a thousand years at the bottom of our hole if your sweet little keys say NO!'

'Bravo!' cried Redempcion, 'next week we'll braid him a raffia key ring!' The nurse did not dare take on Mrs Mingot; she jerked Redempcion by the arm and roughly dragged her towards the door. Somewhere a woman began to sob.

'Martha, don't sob like that!' said a woman. 'Stop sobbing, Martha.'

Mrs Mingot had vanished. The women finally stopped laughing.

The stout man mopped his forehead. 'Calm down, ladies,' he said, 'please calm down!' He did not realize they were already quiet again. 'Let's forget this regrettable incident and the eccentricities of that poor woman. I shall bring you the raffia as I promised. You are too inactive. We must become a community with occupations and interests. Your health depends on it . . . and so does mine. This is our home, at least for the time being, the asylum is our world.'

He was talking to himself. He noticed it probably, because he stopped and walked to the door with slightly stooped shoulders. Rose watched him go. Around her, the hubbub started up again. 'Why did I laugh so hard, a minute ago, at what Mrs Mingot said?' she asked herself.

And then, suddenly, she realized that during those few minutes she had stopped thinking of Paul and that, that really was hell. . . .

'I agree with you about it being hell,' said Mrs Mingot.

Rose wondered if she had been thinking out loud.

'But you have just seen how their creation can turn against them. Do you want me to tell you something? They don't rule us any longer. They've come too late with their kind words and their bundles of straw. Too late. Anarchy is loose, a fire they can't put out now. If they want to get their power back, they'll have to kill us one by one. And I'll be the first to go, I'm fully aware of that!'

A sigh swelled her narrow chest. 'Let's go. It's time for supper.'

Once more the community rites absorbed their attention. Outside, night had fallen.

The evening meal always brought a sort of peace to the women. With calmed faces they sat around the metal tables, in the yellowish light of the ceiling lamps. Hurriedly they emptied their aluminium bowls so that they could have them refilled before the pots were taken away. Suddenly there were fewer crises, fewer lapses.

A full soup spoon dropped noisily on the rim of a bowl, from a distracted hand before it reached the mouth, a piece of bread, thrown at an imaginary animal under the table, a mug of water intentionally spilled on the metal table top – all these merely passed like meteors across the family atmosphere of the meal. The dinner table was a sort of plateau on which almost all the fires of insanity burned out. At table the slightest incongruity seemed to be the beginning of still another madness, much worse and open to unanimous disapproval. Of course this lull did not always extend to the conversations.

'Hey, this may be her last meal!' cried Roubillot.

She pointed her finger at the new woman whose fate had been revealed by the cards. Big Mama Houdin shrugged and went on eating. She did not like to bother with the supernatural unless the cards had been spread out, and especially not at mealtime. But Redempcion who was sitting next to Big Mama Houdin kept nudging her with her elbow.

'Say yes, say yes! And watch her fold up!'

'Redempcion!' cried Mrs Mingot. 'just a little while ago you were praying for her salvation and now you want her to fold up! Who is being fooled here? Am I to assume that you were trying to deceive me and that what you were holding out to her with all that fake fervour was something like bloody wafer? Think back now, think back!'

'When I think back, all I can remember is a monkey's ass that looked like your face,' cried Redempcion.

'Redempcion!' cried Mrs Mingot, 'take that back at once! I curse you, there, I curse you!'

'For God's sake, be quiet,' said Rose, pulling at Mrs Mingot's sleeve.

The wave of pity that had threatened to flood her entire heart a moment ago was gone. 'This is your new family. Go ahead and love them.'

'Aren't you eating any more?' asked Mrs Mingot. 'I can see you're all worked up. Did you find a pebble in the lentils? Or maybe you're still thinking about your husband, and that, too, must be hard to chew. . . .'

She had raised her voice for the others to hear. She was trying for a comeback after Redempcion's insult; and besides, her friendship with Rose was over, she spat on it, she spat on all friendships. Ah, they didn't know a thing about her! They didn't know what it meant to be a rebel!

5*

'But he's just a blotter, that husband of yours!' she continued with a strange laugh. 'What a lot of tears he needs! So many tears, and you're certainly not stingy. . . .'

Rose said nothing. 'A living husband,' she repeated to herself, 'a living husband. . . . .'

A living husband, a perfect husband, a unique husband.

Long before endowing him, as now, with all the virtues of resurrection, Rose had been conscious of how perfectly he fitted into each one of her moulds. Even his appearance seemed to be making an effort: not too tall, not too short, not too handsome, not too ugly. And it was the same for his moral virtues. The system proceeded by absences, by default. A living husband, a perfect husband, a unique husband meant a pruned-down husband. 'How cruel I am,' thought Rose, wiping her eyes with her sheet.

Subjecting him like this to the despotism of analysis made her cry faster than anything else. Her love was her tears. In her mind she wilfully mistreated the beloved image, shot cynical darts at the soft target, arrows of lucidity superior to love, dismissed the image, made it disappear, brought it back with an impudent jolt: she discovered the rites of sacrilege.

Drunk to tears with blasphemy, after evoking a reality that left her exhausted, unable to move, with eyes burning and her heart open, there remained his name, this word, this syllable 'Paul'.

Like a family of invisible pet birds, dozens of first names lived within the asylum walls. Last names had not followed them. Flown from the nests of distant birth certificates, the first names led, in this place where they had taken refuge, the nimble, naïve life of souls who have left their bodies.

Big Mama Houdin often spoke of Gabriel – her son, her brother, her husband, no one knew. Julia Vuillaume sometimes spoke of Bertha; an old white-haired woman talked of Louis. Through her tears Martha called for a Martha who was not herself, or else what was one to think? Among these fluttered, less frequently, like migratory birds intercepted on a long-distance flight or creations from some faraway sunny island, Charleses, Octavians, Luciens, Albertas, Peters and Bertrands, some croaking nostalgically, others chirping meekly into the night of oblivion which was falling all around them, or else soon exhausted, silenced by the brief, deceptive splendour of a dawn. Among them Paul, flying steadily, untiringly.

The first time he had flown, with a dull flapping of nocturnal wings as though still blind, and frightened by the closeness of these unknown walls, it had been in that hotel by the sea where, from the ordinary vacation Rose had come to spend, she had begun slipping into another kind of vacation with wider, airier horizons: a vacation from her sanity.

Since then, what flights, what metamorphoses! Sometimes she strode through life with a falcon on her fist, her eyes looking straight ahead, closing the whole world into her hunting preserve; at other times, during the brief carnal moments of love, she had watched a macaw unfold his wide wings, like a stiff, quivering, multi-coloured fan; with closed claws he leaned backwards, never letting go of his perch bar; sometimes she had followed the circlings of a hawk; with eyes slitted from too much sun; sometimes she had listened to the satiated sleep of a dove. . . .

'It's clear that Rose Schmidt will always be the last one to go downstairs!' exclaimed a nurse, holding open the dormitory door and impatiently jangling her keys.

Rose was stuffing objects into a little bag that Mrs Mingot had made for her out of an old black satin lining, at the time of their friendship; things acquired at the price of endless patience, sometimes due to the blind, chaotic generosity of those women for whom the hour of giving had struck (when, a moment later, the hour of taking back struck, they stood in the middle of the room, motionless and dispossessed, their memory suddenly empty), things one found in the courtyard or in the washrooms, things which no longer belonged to anyone.

A comb with a few teeth missing, an empty match box for needles, or stamps, a sharp-edged scrap of mirror (nothing has such pointed angles, such curves, as a broken mirror), a red cardboard wallet that leaves suspicious traces on the moist towel one has taken along, an empty tin box, still powdery inside from the sugar coating of cough drops, an old, torn book, chapters five and six of a story that takes place in Scotland, those were the things put to anonymous use, things on which ownership left no mark. By losing them, by giving them at random to the first woman one met (in the hour of giving that always struck at a moment of loneliness and just after one had cried), one returned them to a collective need which reached everywhere and which washed them of the marks and memories of possession.

By their very anonymity these objects became a kind of incongruous currency. Still, the desire for ownership was strong enough so that each woman felt the urge to drag around a cloth pocket dangling from a finger by a string that one wound and unwound incessantly.

'Rose Schmidt, how much longer are you going to stuff junk into that bag?'

Rose hurried to the door with a feeling that she had forgotten something. Just in case, she passed her hand through her hair while the nurse slammed the dormitory door behind her. Rose ran down the stone steps, her little black cloth bag bouncing against her legs. She had returned to her simplicity. True, the memory of Paul hardly ever left her, but neither did the little black cloth bag, this bag filled with miserable essentials. Finally she reached the big room, where winter (perhaps only a spring that resembled winter) continued to keep the women indoors. For a moment surprise held her nailed to the threshold. She had pushed the door open and hesitated to close it behind her.

Disregarding all proportions, it was like a living tree, a monkey arbour, a human-sized ant heap. During the first seconds, life, movement denied any identity, any separate existence, because the milling about of the women untiringly substituted one face for another. The voices copied each other, fused into one another, answered a question with a similar question, mingled with echoes, questioned questions, answered answers. A woman who had just called out in one direction suddenly ran off in another, while a different woman appeared in her place, her mouth open from a cry she had not uttered, offered to an absurd fate.

Some women remained glued to the wall like blue stains, then came running up, suddenly voluminous, heavy with a kind of excessive presence, and turned abruptly as though snatched up in the sliding of a convex mirror. There never seemed to be a moment of rest within the sweaty walls, which steamed as though they contained a furiously boiling stew

Rose stepped into the room and everything around her seemed to calm down. Roubillot passed and winked maliciously, followed by three little girls, round-eyed and intent like small fish swimming after the larger ones. Mrs Mingot came up to Rose.

'I'm not talking to you any more! For two days you have constantly pretended not to know me. I've become too disreputable, uh? Well, let me tell you, you haven't heard the last of me!'

Rose was going to protest, but the old woman had already disappeared. The confusion had started again all around her, the threads that hummed around the shuttle, the madness, the roar of the looms. She brushed her hand over her forehead. She, too, was going to join the dance, she, too, was going to set to work, she was going to spin again. . . .

During a whole period of that winter (or of that spring that so much resembled winter) Rose turned in circles. She started in the morning, as soon as she came down from the dormitory. She thought that it would be on a day like this that Paul would come. About ten o'clock she allowed herself a break and went to sit on a bench, near the other women, silent as she, attentive to the signs of their illness. By that time Rose had walked around the room at least a hundred times. With her eyes she measured the surface of the area; in her mind she estimated the job still to be done, with the calm determination of workmen sitting by the scaffolding during their lunch hour.

The success of each turn around the room depended on two conditions: the first was of a strictly technical nature. Each time you tried to walk the greatest possible distance, hugging the walls and keeping the same pace. This required that none of the other women who were wandering about the room come over to block your path. The corners of the room with the change of direction they required punctuated the walk rather pleasantly. If no one got in your way or blocked the corner, obliging you to take a short cut or a detour, you turned with perfectly regularity, you became the wife of time.

The second condition for success was more difficult to define. But it was good, at any rate, to take the date of whatever day it was, for a starting point (no one knew the date; one had to ask a nurse who often answered with anything that came into her head) or simply take the seasons: winter, spring, summer, autumn, and then go backwards from one year to the next.

Rain, if it happened to be raining outside, could also serve as a pretext and call up memories of other rainy days. But there are all sorts of rains: first of all there is summer rain and winter rain; there are a lot of subtle differences in the rustling, the light, the odour of each rain.

Rarer, snow was also more reliable: memories inscribed themselves black on white. Thus, the wind, the date: February twenty-third, night falling at five o'clock, could suggest a new subject for meditations every day, retrieve from the bottom of memory a less lonely season with a lighter sky than the one outside.

But in the afternoon, or towards evening, suddenly the thought – like a cry, suppressed all day: 'When will I see him again? Will I ever see him again?' The lamps had been lit. Shadows were ambling across the floor, naked reefs, hurdles, black outlines inviting one to fail. Rose sat down on the bench, stretched her tired legs and rediscovered her companions, as fresh as in the first hour, animated by the nervousness of night.

Sometimes she searched through the crowd for Mrs Mingot. She was not at all surprised at the radical change in behaviour that made the old woman seek out the loudest and most rebellious women in the section. Such metamorphoses were common here. Freedom fermenting inside, the calls, the temptations of freedom, blood kicking in the veins could throw one very quickly into far greater excesses than insanity.

For the last couple of days Mrs Mingot had been letting go with a violence of which Rose had not thought her capable. She hardly ever left the gang formed by Redempcion, Gertrude, Roubillot and one or two of her disciples, with Big Mama Houdin sitting close by like a sleeping sage, an asthmatic adviser. For a long time Mrs Mingot had been considered an arrogant woman with a weakness for denunciations. Only thanks to her scene with the director had she been admitted into the circle which, moreover, at the slightest provocation – and often as a game – broke up and regrouped itself far from her, at the other end of the room a moment after she had been admitted. At those moments Rose could see Mrs Mingot rapidly crossing the room, trying hard to hide her confusion under a grimace of fiendish joy, an air of rowdiness, a painful exaggeration of the subversive sentiments that were to allow her back into the mocking, evasive circle.

Sometimes Rose was tempted to go up to her former companion. Hadn't Mrs Mingot plunged into these excesses because of her disappointment in friendship? 'I talked too much about Paul. I locked myself into my memories. She came to me on the first day, she guided me, offered me her chatty, cordial presence, her relentless, ardent friendship at a time when everything was slipping. As soon as I was able to come back to life, to my life, find my past again, I turned away from her,' Rose told herself. But she didn't budge. It was too late.

Even if it was through disappointment and bitterness, Mrs Mingot had found a form of new life, a new fate. She who had always talked of hell was now pushing it to extremes. She was fanning the flames of her truth. One night she tried to set fire to the asylum.

Patiently she had stuffed her little sack full of bits of paper, rags soaked with grease and oil during meals, twigs she had picked up in the yard. No one ever found out how she was able to get hold of matches.

She had slipped out of the room and sneaked into a linen closet on the second floor where sheets lay folded on wooden shelves. When she reappeared, she winked to the women of the gang who were awaiting her return in a state of excitement occasionally heightened by gestures of panic. The secret had been let out long before she came back. The whispering brought the news to Rose who was stopping from her rounds. 'Mingot' – since her plunge into insubordination she was hardly ever called 'Mrs' any more – 'Mingot has just set fire to the linen closet.' Why the linen closet, wondered Rose.

'Good work! They drive us crazy with their linen!' said a woman near her.

'But we'll be burned alive ' screamed another woman, jumping up. 'We're locked in!'

She rushed to the door. Others followed.

'Fire! Fire!' they began to screech.

Through the glass door of the room they could see smoke coming down the staircase. Nurses were running in all directions. Everywhere alarm bells started ringing. The screams of the women were deafening. At last the doors to the courtyard were opened. The women ran out on to the soggy lawn. Night was falling. Calls answered each other throughout the gardens, under the trees, dragged out beyond the walls. The director drove up in a car, with men in black. The brakes screeched to a stop on the gravel. Somewhere, a church bell was ringing. No flames were yet visible.

In the darkness Rose looked for Mrs Mingot. She found her in the centre of a group of women, pale, speechless. She was replying to the questions they were asking her with a mere nod of the head, trying to smile like an exhausted champion on the verge of collapse who is being congratulated for his victory.

'Leave her alone,' Rose said to the women.

She took Mrs Mingot's arm and pulled her towards the end of the courtyard. The firemen arrived, and the women gathered round the engine. Walking closely along the asylum walls, Rose and Mrs Mingot reached a deserted spot. Rose recognized it as the place where, so many times at the beginning of her internment, she had sat with Mrs Mingot.

'Do you remember?' said Mrs Mingot who also recognized the spot and came out of her silence with a slightly weary voice. 'How hot it was then! When was it? A year ago? Two years ago?'

'Eight months,' said Rose.

'Ah, you were all wedged into yourself at that time,' pursued Mrs Mingot. 'The first days you never opened your mouth. And eyes as big as saucers. Saucers full of water, because you were crying. You've always cried a lot here.'

'I cry much less now,' said Rose, her throat taut.

'God, how hot it was! Sometimes I'd say to you: Come, Rose, let's sit in the shade, or you'll be ready for Section Three. . . .'

'Yes,' said Rose.

'And now it is I who am ready for Section Three,' pursued Mrs Mingot, hanging her head. 'You won't see me again, Rose, never again. No one here will see me again. One day you'll hear that I died, and I'll have been dead for a long time. They don't keep you informed here,' she added in a carefully distinct voice, no longer her own.

'Mrs Mingot . . .' stammered Rose.

'Never mind, Rose, don't say anything,' murmured Mrs Mingot, lifting a shaking hand. Her voice was about to break. She got hold of herself again. 'Yes, how you used to cry! And Paul? Where do you stand with him now?'

Policemen had come into the yard. They took big steps, walking one behind the other.

'Sometimes I have the feeling that he'll come any moment,' answered Rose. 'He'll take me away with him at once. You know, we are such a perfectly united couple. It makes people smile, they don't believe such fidelity exists, such a unique love. And yet you only have to see him, see him look at me, to understand. His eyes become all golden. One always thinks that I am boasting. But it's really true; besides, his love, this almost excessive love, I admit, I return it completely: he is my life. Sometimes, I think he must be dead or he would have come. But that's impossible. I would have known; something, at that very moment, would have snapped inside me. . . .'

'Don't worry,' said Mrs Mingot, 'he is not dead . . . and he still loves you. I can tell you now: I don't feel him dead. My own death, yes. But what do we matter, you and I! Life is all outside of us. We must put an end to this hell, Rose! Life means the others. . . . Rose, Rose!' she cried very quickly, 'here we are, you and I, against the wall. How hot it was! I used to tell you my stories. . . . No, no don't cry! Don't cry, Rose, please don't cry, do you remember, that's from the opera "The Dragoons of Villars". Rose. . . .'

The fire had already been put out. The firemen were rolling up their hoses, talking loudly into the night. The policemen filed out through the gates. Nurses were calling the roll, shouting the women's names, rushing about everywhere in the thickening darkness.

'Don't cry, Rose,' Mrs Mingot said again.

Men were coming towards them, led by the director.

'Sorry, Mrs Mingot, you'll have to come with us,' he said softly.

The old woman bent down and tore a small dead leaf from a bush, blackened with frost. Two male nurses in white smocks had seized her without harshness, each taking an arm. Mrs Mingot raised her hand, the little dead leaf trembling between her fingers. Already they were taking her away.

'Look, Rose, Rose!' she cried, 'do you remember: it's freezing. . . .'

A voice from the distance, slightly theatrical, slightly broken. They led Rose back into the flooded dining hall where, this evening, the women sat quietly.

And life went on within the high asylum walls. The summer (perhaps only a spring that resembled summer) came again, and the leaves. Again they went out into the courtyard, white-washed with sun. Stimulated by the fire, by the damage it had done, and especially by those flames that seemed ready to soar up again at any moment and whose existence the fire had revealed, the director undertook what he called a reorganization of the services. They finally did receive raffia and straw.

Rose was chosen to direct the workshop which, in good weather, was set up under the trees, with women singing in off-key voices. They braided little mats, baskets, sandals, sun hats. The director took a great interest in the work and spent long moments sitting beside Rose, smoking a cigar.

'Rose Schmidt,' he began. 'I always tell you that we ought to have a little chat, just you and I. And then, when I sit here beside you, as at this moment, with a few minutes to spare, I don't feel like talking about you and your past any more. I look at you: you are calm, perfectly lucid, a bit dreamy perhaps. I say to myself: but she knows, she remembers. But in your presence, Rose Schmidt, I begin to believe that conscience and memory exist only when one accepts them. And perhaps reality only exists when one wants it.

'I also tell myself that one invents less in lies and dreams than in a confession. Yes, all those things, all that you represent behind your smiling, closed face, is very disturbing, Rose Schmidt, very disturbing. And I prefer to see you here, living in your false hopes, than dying somewhere else of real despair. Above all I bet on life, and against reason. I take part in your game. The seasons take part in it, too: you live. But I talk and talk and you don't answer, and you're right not to answer. Your reason is stronger than mine. You alone, after all, know how to deny. That is a great virtue. Very rare. Your love exists in spite of everything, Rose Schmidt, and I am happy to be its helper. . . .'

He got up, put his hand on Rose's shoulder and walked off under the trees.

'Red, three strands, Annette,' said Rose. 'No, not raspberry red. Cherry red. Thank you. Two green. . . . Straw now, a whole handful while you're at it: that's for the bottom. . . .'

The silence of the summer afternoon settled down, hardly troubled by the women's talk: 'The handles, Redempcion, we're waiting!' 'Oh, you old needle thief, you devil, you!'

Insanity was still there, under the asylum trees, but so was summer, so was hope.

'Six blue, please, Annette,' said Rose. 'No, change this one. Look, it's badly dyed. . . .'

She wiped a few drops of sweat from her forehead with the back of her hand, looked at the light-flooded sky. The images of life were there: this chatty community, easily delirious, in the midst of which Rose was establishing her power a little more each day; her authority grew, those humble daily tasks, the play of blue strands, and red, and yellow, and green, in which insanity was gradually trapping itself, the past forgiven, summer in the leaves. Rose was dreaming, with idle hands, her eyes far away. It was good not to know just yet, not yet to want to remember.

translated by Ursule Molinaro and Venable Herndon

The Little Square

WHEN A storm was brewing, I watched it approach above the baker's house. Not that this house was any lower than the others that crowded around the little square, but the round, sun-bleached tiles of its roof rose to the west and reflected the whole sky.

On the calmest days, when the wind barely disturbed the smoke that rose from the oven chimney, I watched large white clouds appear slowly above the rooftop of the bakery. They did not grow dark until much later, and for a long time kept a fringe of light. Then, heavy with shadows, the storm anticipated dusk and drew a low sky down upon the world.

The baker's house, with its oven that opened on to the little square, stood against the motionless, gradually fading light of the sky, then against the darkening clouds, and finally against the first gusts of the storm that beat the smoke down upon its roof and over the square in a fiery whirlwind.

The glow from the oven flickered now and then in the dark, low-ceilinged room where two men, with gaunt white torsos naked in the firelight, baked large batches of bread one after the other. When the oven became red hot, they emptied the live coals into immense, black iron drums as tall as the ten-year-old child that I then was, and left them to smoulder and die in front of the bakery door.

Then the square, already warm from the blazing sunshine before the storm, seemed to catch fire. It burned with a deep, suffocating glow, like a blind inferno in the heat of summer. When I came near the drums, I could hear the crunching of the wooden embers as they became charcoal. Later, in the bakery, deserted by the bakers who had left for a drink, the formations of hot loaves also gave out a crisping sound, like grasshoppers in a sunburnt meadow.

When I shut my eyes, the heavy, abundant aroma of the bread seemed like an emanation from the scorched earth as it awaited the storm. Some of the burning shadows from the empty oven seemed to have escaped into the sky. A little grey train of ashes blew out of the open door of the bakery into the middle of the square, and soon mingled with the dust, raised by a black hen who was ruffling her feathers.

The first drops of rain sometimes fell before the coals in the big kettles had cooled off, and sizzled on the lids where I had been trying in vain to cook little pancakes made of dough stolen from the bakery.

I went back to our house on the other side of the square and stayed under the edge of the roof, watching the rain fall and the clouds race by. Across from where I stood, the oven was being stoked for a new batch of bread. Smoke billowed forth, struggled with the wind, and sometimes blew a volley of sparks against the storm-blackened sky.

Below, in the glowing interior, the two white bodies moved about, and the bakery appeared to me like the hold of a ship, with smoke swept back by the storm. The heavy odours had disappeared; the wind gave a watery freshness to the air. The rain had extinguished the bread.

There was more than just the storms. There were winter days when the heat from the kettles created a zone of welcome around the threshold of the bakery, with whirlwinds of flour and ashes, like fine snow. When the oven door was opened, and quickly shut, the aroma of the hot bread broke through the frosty silence like an utterance suddenly overheard. Winter gave the bread a voice.

But whether storms threatened the square with rain, or frost hardened the earth, or spring sent flights of pigeons into the morning sky, or a gentle mist fell at the end of the day, the baker's wife was always on the run. . . .

This was the wife of the younger man; the father and son worked together. She was quite tall, and dark, and wore an anxiously hopeful expression. She would close the windowed door of the bakery behind her and stand motionless on the threshold, looking over the square, and then, when she felt that it was sufficiently deserted, she started out.

She ran straight ahead, her hands clasped in front of her chest, kicking her feet out to the side as if fettered by her skirt. She would go as far as the other side of the square, slightly to the left of our house, where there was a shed belonging to the bakery. This sheltered an old truck used to deliver bread to the outlying farms.

The baker's wife stepped into the shed, rearranged her black hair, and then turned and ran back across the empty square.

Reaching the threshold of the bakery, she peered through the flour-soiled panes of glass, as if to make sure that neither of the two bakers had noticed her, and then, if no one had appeared in the square, she would run back to the shed, and return again. . . . These manœuvres went on for several minutes, then, out of breath or feeling herself watched, she would go back into the bakery.

One hour later she would hurry forth again. On a good day she would continue these impetuous goings and comings, this aimless and confined wandering until she was exhausted. I would see her, paler than when she started, pressing her hand to her heart before she went into the bakery. A kind of contentment or joy illuminated her face, as if she had somehow been saved.

But this salvation did not last. Before the morning or afternoon was over I would again see the baker's wife appear
anxiously on the threshold, clasping her nervous hands in
prayer before her, ready for flight. My presence did not bother
her. I played on the ground, often in her path, and her heels
clattered next to my ear under a flurry of black petticoats. The
tendons above her calves were strong, but delicately shaped.
The baker's wife barely avoided me. A few inches closer, and
she would have stepped over me.

She paid just as little attention to the other inhabitants of the
town, who carried on the same occupations every day in front
of their houses. The old woman dressed in black with her back
turned, leaning over a tub of laundry, the fruit dealer who was
slowly piling up his crates stained by the juicy fruit of summer,
the blacksmith . . .

His shop was set into an alleyway in the corner of the square.
It was a dark, out-of-the-way place, paved with stones from
the river, where the fire burned with a blue sulphuric vapour
or a red glow kindled by the bellows. There reigned an odour
of burnt horn, of hot iron and the pain of animals.

Horses were shod outside. They would lose their balance
and skid on the rounded cobblestones. The blacksmith's son,
bending over with his hands interlaced as if to help someone
mount, would support their whole weight against his leather
apron. He was a boy with a white forehead and a shock of dark
hair. He had just come back from the army and spoke very
little. When the horse, drowsy from the ordeal of the shoeing,
slipped back against him, he would bite his lip.

Oxen and cows, who were often put in harness in this region,
were shod inside the shop in a dung-soiled wooden apparatus
called a 'trave'.

The animal was suspended in a leather girth and lifted by
pulleys into the middle of a quivering scaffold where wooden
frames were closed over its stiffened shanks. It would go on
bucking for a long time, immobilized, its struggles only shook
the creaking pillory. As it swung back and forth, fury turned

into a gentle roll, the desperate effort into waves of jerky pitching. In the glimmering darkness of the shop, lit by the smoky fires of the forge that made the trave cast immense shadows against the wall, like masts webbed with taut ropes, a cow, caught in the rigging, sailed through the air.

On this side of the square, in the suffocating shadows of the alleyway, everything was slow-moving and violent, with wintry shadows, a glow of coals or short blue flames, an odour of charcoal or horn beneath smoky walls where horseshoes hung like ranked shields. A fire of silent suffering burned there, stoked by weariness communicating itself through the long hours of the day to the two men who stood driving nails into the hooves of animals.

How bright the bakery would have seemed, with its gay, dancing flames and the inviting aroma of the bread, had I not known that the heat of the storm, or the stifling air of dusk was enough to corrupt its virtues, to bring damnation even upon the bread and transform the bakery into a white inferno, suffocating in goodness!

Even on ordinary days, when the air was clear and light, or in the spring when the two bakers were in a good mood and let me come in to gather bits of dough from their kneading board, for the little cakes which I would never succeed in cooking on the charcoal drums and which I would never be able to eat, even then, I realized that the simple joys of this house consecrated to the idyll of bread-making could become monotonous and cruel.

It was probably in search of a more spacious freedom that the dark woman was already running. People said that she was vain, that she was trying to keep a slim figure with these repeated exercises. Some made excuses for her; everyone knew that the smell of fresh bread, breathed day after day, was nourishing, even fattening if one stayed sedentary. Besides, the baker was jealous; he never let his wife go into the village alone.

Under his hair, stiffened and whitened by the flour, the face of the young baker expressed a kind of sad bewilderment. Sometimes he would appear on the threshold, stripped to the waist, bent and shivering like a swimmer who has been caught by dusk and is waiting for a free bathhouse to dress in. He watched his wife run towards the shed, and when she returned, still running, he made her go inside the bakery where I saw her making wild, impatient gestures, illuminated by the glow from the oven.

I guessed that the baker was angry with his wife for making a spectacle of herself in front of the inhabitants of the square. She probably thought that they were absorbed by their chores, too used to watching her run back and forth to pay any attention. I knew otherwise. They were less indifferent than they seemed.

Perhaps one could overlook the sleepy gaze of the fat old woman dressed in black who had made her fortune in the canneries and who sat, from spring until fall, on her wooden balcony decorated with nasturtiums, or the dull eyes (in themselves the colour of laundry) of the other old woman who drew herself up for a moment over her tub, or maybe even the pitiless glance of the fruit dealer, a dry bald man who balanced his piles of crates with one hand as he watched the baker's wife. He called her a whore, under his breath. I stood near him and though I did not understand the word very well, I knew that it was an insult. But the insult mattered very little, no more than the glances of all these other silent witnesses.

There was only one gaze in the whole square that mattered, a heavy burning one that was painful in its intensity and made me worried. It was the gaze of the blacksmith's son.

The boy stood slightly hunched, holding the horse's hoof in both hands as he looked out into the square. The father carried the red-hot horseshoe back from the forge, placed it on the hoof which began to smoke, and through this bitter little cloud the son went on watching the baker's wife.

When there were no horses to be shod, he lingered in front of the shop, puttering about, picking up the long cuneiform nails that the blacksmith had dropped between the cobble-stones. Then, standing up, he stayed there with his fist full of nails, watching the dark woman run. When he stood like that, the blacksmith's son looked dangerous to me.

I was not the only one who was somewhat afraid of him. The inhabitants of the square talked about him in low voices, say-ing that he was losing his mind. He had always been silent and moody, and this was usually the first symptom of such an illness. Sometimes, in the middle of the day, he would carry a pail of water to the door of the shop, dip into it with both hands, and then splash it again and again over his head.

He was pale, with a wild look in his eye. For a long time he stood there with his wet hands held against his face, as though he were in pain and the cool water were the only remedy, or as though the only remedy were to hold his palms crushed against his eyes and not to see anything.

Yet, in his hard expression, behind the almost cruel intensity of his eyes when he watched the baker's wife as she ran across the square, I discovered a note of brightness, of desire, of joy....

The baker, who had just stepped out the front door and stood there, rubbing his naked shoulders, was too far away to see the change that lightened the face of the blacksmith's son under his look of suffering. Nevertheless he pushed his wife inside the bakery as soon as she ran up to him. His gestures were firm, but gentle. He was protecting his wife from some danger which I could only dimly imagine from the way the blacksmith's son stood there, with a dark, transparent gleam in his eye.

Earlier, as he watched his wife run, the baker had appeared not to notice the blacksmith's son who stood with his fists clenched in the corner of the square. It was said to be dangerous to look at a madman; the look of another human being could ignite their smouldering aggressions, bring them into the open by giving them an object.

For a few days, I myself had stopped watching the black-smith's son except out of the corner of my eye, or when he was not standing, stiff and erect, at the corner of the square. He had stolen the square from me, had appropriated it with his intense stare, and now I thought that I could smell a stronger, harsher odour of horn and burning coals coming from the forge.

Before that, the square had belonged to me, with its small leaning elm tree that I used to climb, shinnying up the trunk, its rivulets of dirty water where I drowned flies, the western sky that slipped over the roof of the bakery, all its peacefulness that was now defiled by one solitary gaze, and disturbed, too, by so many averted pairs of eyes.

Out of caution, I followed the baker's example and averted my own, and it was just at this time that the dark-haired woman who ran back and forth across the square began to return the glances of the blacksmith's son.

I noticed that from then on she left the bakery either when her husband and her father-in-law went to have a drink in the kitchen, or on the days when her husband went to deliver the bread to distant farms, As she ran between the bakery and the shed, the baker's wife would look two or three times at the blacksmith's son who moved forward, step by step, to the edge of the paved yard in front of his shop. At first he kept his fists tightly clenched and then, when the dark-haired woman had looked at him several times, and was about to pass him, he opened them and ran his hands slowly along the sides of his leather apron.

As for me, I could see nothing in the glances of the baker's wife. Nothing but great seriousness. It was one of those adult glances, fraught with shadows and interrupted by much fluttering of the eyelids, that made me think there was not enough bread or that someone was about to die.

The fruit dealer, whom I often visited because he gave me staves from his crates to make into aeroplanes, encouraged my fears. He, too, caught the looks exchanged by the woman who ran by with her hands clasped on her chest, and the blacksmith's son, who stood there, paler than ever. The fruit dealer muttered under his breath that it would come to a bad end.

When? I watched the sky over the baker's house. It moved as slowly as before, bearing clouds, or gilded with light, and I asked myself whether its darkening and brightening reflected our existence, whether men's lives sent up flares or shadows, and whether, on the day when something came to a bad end in the little square, as the fruit dealer had warned, a new eclipse, a more lurid storm, or a heavier fog would loom upon us.

Meanwhile the square became the battleground for mysterious forces. Never had I felt so confined, or worse still, so unwanted. The baker was annoyed to see me there all day. I was no longer allowed in the bakery and if I came near, he shouted at me, telling me to go play somewhere else in the village, in the alley behind our house, or with the other children who played near the church. Why was I so nosy, always hanging around the square?

But I wasn't being nosy. Those who were there all around me never paid any attention to me, and I looked at them as I looked at the earth, the sky, the trunk of the elm tree, or my flies as they drowned in dirty puddles. They were a part of what I received from life, without searching, without really being given anything. . . .

I did not answer the baker, but as I turned away I had the sad feeling that wickedness had invaded my little square. Everything seemed dark and gloomy, even though the sky remained the same, and I told myself that perhaps these invisible shadows, this subtle ageing of the light were what darkened the bad days, the days when something came to a bad end, in houses or squares.

The baker's wife was still running. Sometimes her husband called aloud to her. The blacksmith's son watched her from the corner of the square. His pallor, the tremendous strain that showed on his face seemed to have communicated themselves to the baker's wife. Now she looked at him more often, and sometimes crumpled her handkerchief between her hands.

Would they never speak to one another? The intensity of their silence frightened me. It weighed upon me as I sat on the ground and smoothed the dust with the palm of my hand. The whole little square became mute. The inhabitants seemed to have laid aside their tasks for a moment, waiting for this sudden oppression to cease. Now and then the baker came out and called his wife. She disappeared into the bakery. Then life went on, quietly. . . . Yes, it would all end badly. Every day the silence grew a little bit heavier.

And then, one morning, the horse came.

It was a black horse with a sleek coat, one of the half-breds that the farmers harnessed to their light carts. He had just been shod and the blacksmith was carrying his tools back into the shop when the horse started towards the middle of the square. The blacksmith's son, who had taken him out of harness, stood by without attempting to catch him.

The baker's wife was running across the square. She saw the horse coming towards her. He was walking and the noise of his new shoes made him nervous. The woman ran into the shed. Its shadows and wide door probably looked to the horse like a stable, and he came closer. The baker's wife had backed up against the radiator of the truck, motionless and terrified. The horse stood facing her, throwing its head back now and again, waiting for her to speak, or just surprised not to be able to enter.

Then I saw the blacksmith's son come forward. He was not running. He walked with a tense, rather swift step, and a pale, preoccupied look on his face, like someone who has hurt himself and is about to bleed. He came up to the horse and stayed there, without moving, watching the baker's wife. She stared at him, also very intently. Several inhabitants of the square stood on their doorsteps. They watched the scene in silence. I waited for the door of the bakery to open. It did not open. It seemed to me as if the black horse had begun to tremble.

All of a sudden, as though it had pierced the deep shadows that still surrounded me, as though it had finally been identified amidst so much nameless reality, something began to take shape in my mind.

I realized that whatever animated this horse, the power of its muscles, the neighing as yet unheard, a dream of spaces more open than space, all that lived within it, also lived within this man and this woman who stood looking at each other in silence.

The baker's wife finally lowered her eyes. The blacksmith's son took the horse by the bridle and led it slowly back to the corner of the square. The horse seemed worn out. It was not yet noon but in the square one would have thought that it was evening. The baker's wife stayed in the shed a minute more. She kept her head lowered. When she lifted it, just as she came out of the door and started to run, I saw that her face was pink, or rather, illuminated. The baker's wife seemed beautiful to me. She crossed the square, under the eyes of its inhabitants, and closed the bakery door behind her, No one was there; the baker had seen nothing.

Then I knew that the days foretold by the fruit dealer were near. Everyone now knew why the baker's wife ran back and forth across the square. She did not have to run to keep thin, people said, love alone would keep her from growing fat. And this love, in spite of the distance across the square, in spite of the silence, grew more and more triumphant.

The blacksmith's son did not have the bewildered look in his eyes any more, the look that made him seem destined for a strait jacket. Nor was he seen dousing his head at length in a pail of water. When the baker's wife was running, he came out into the square, slightly beyond the paved yard of his shop, and stared at her calmly, holding a cigarette in his hand. He left his leather apron inside, buttoned up his black shirt, and stood there as men do at a ball, watching the girl they intend to ask for the next dance. His expression did not change until the baker's wife went back to the ovens. The blacksmith's son did not go right back to the forge; he finished his cigarette, looking nervously in the direction of the bakery.

Sometimes, while the blacksmith's son was still standing there, the baker came out to fetch some water. He pretended not to see the boy, but as he walked back from the well, his jaw was clenched and he winced, as if the pails were heavier than usual.

One day soon, I thought, the two men would have to come to blows. The fruit dealer thought so, too, but having been from the beginning on the side of the baker, he feared the cruelty of his rival. He thought him perfectly capable of using a piece of iron, and the baker was naked to the waist.

He was naked to the waist as he came forward into the square, on the day when everything seemed ready to come to a head. It was market day; wagons crowded the square. The farmers left them there early in the morning, piled up against each other in all directions, and led their horses into the stable that belonged to the café.

The shafts of the wagons, some pointing at the sky, others leaning on the ground and crossing each other, looked like a nautical scene, without sails, or a devastated forest. To me they were ships, and each wheel became a helm. Between the polished shafts the sky seemed to speed by more swiftly. There was also the space beneath the wagons where I sat, as though in the hold of a ship, under a ceiling of rough-hewn boards.

I was there, sitting on the ground, in the lattice of all the wagon wheels, when I recognized the legs of the baker's wife. I pulled myself up between the shafts to watch her. She stepped gingerly over each one on her way to the shed. She had to grope her way along, for many of the tilted wagons were hooded and extended above her head. She may have been a little disoriented, but that did not explain why she lingered on the way and leaned against a wheel, lifting her face to the sky with an expression of patient longing.

Suddenly I heard a step behind me, between the wagons, and I ducked down next to the ground. A man was moving behind the wheels. I recognized the shoes, stained with coal and water, and the black trousers; it was the blacksmith's son. He was circling around between the wagons, leaping nimbly over the shafts. He soon found the baker's wife, Hearing someone approach, she grew still, her back against a wheel.

I did not hear what they were saying. Were they only talking? They stood facing each other, with their legs touching. The blacksmith's son had placed his hands on the woman's hips. Her hands were behind her, gripping the spokes of the wheel. After a few minutes, the woman stirred, and the wheel turned ever so slightly, grinding into the earth.

Someone began to call, far beyond the forest of wagons. It was the baker who had begun to worry when his wife did not return. He called her by her first name. Her name was Simone. His voice was both stern and plaintive. Simone and the blacksmith's son, their legs entwined, seemed to lean even harder against the wheel, which moved again.

Were they deaf, or unaware of the danger? No, just then they separated for a second, listened, and then clasped each other once more. It was as if they wished to enhance their pleasure by that strange shudder, that excruciating but wilful anguish which I felt at the moment of being discovered when I played cops and robbers with my schoolfriends, and which I now experienced with them. I realized that they wanted fear to give them the illusion of being pressed one against the other, naked.

The baker, still calling, wandered among the wagons. He finally began to come near and the blacksmith's son, keeping his head low, moved swiftly and silently away. Then the baker's wife answered her husband. Was he idiotic enough to think that she was lost? I crawled underneath the wagons, on all fours. I saw the baker. He was standing, stripped to the waist and slightly hunched over, among all the shafts. He still did not see his wife. I hid from him. He was right near me. Between the spokes of a wheel, I could see that his whole body was trembling.

From then on, the baker's wife appeared in the square less often. She only ran across when her husband had gone to the country to deliver his bread. She would disappear for quite a while in the shed. The blacksmith's son also went out less

6

often, and he barely raised his head as if he were shoeing a horse when the baker's wife ran across the square.

The fruit dealer said, however, that he still had his doubts. His anxiety reassured me. I waited for the next market day. When it arrived, I found myself a place beneath the wagons, early in the morning. The first thing I heard was a newly-shod horse being backed up between the shafts of a carriage. I came closer, being careful to keep hidden. The blacksmith's son was harnessing a black horse to a covered cart, a horse just like the one that he had let loose in the square a few days before. When the harness was fastened, the blacksmith's son remained by the horse, caressing it with his hand.

Then I heard a familiar step resounding hurriedly across the square. The baker's wife was running between the wagons, towards the shed. When she came out she was carrying a small wicker suitcase. She walked towards the harnessed carriage. The blacksmith's son whistled softly to guide her towards him. He helped her climb up, and she slipped beneath the hood of the cart.

I stood up. The blacksmith's son, who was about to step into the driver's seat, saw me. He put a finger to his lips, asking me to keep silent. He questioned me with his eyes. I nodded. The blacksmith's son jumped into the cart, and holding the reins, guided the horse out of the square. The wheels clattered for a long time on the rounded cobblestones and then I heard no more. A few minutes later, the baker came and called his wife. He talked to himself, alone among the wagons and crossed his arms over his chest, rubbing his bare shoulders. He looked intently at me. I turned away.

The owner of the black horse found a letter in the forge telling him that he would find his horse and cart at a large town nearby. The baker almost went out of his mind. Sometimes he could be seen, in a black jacket, sitting on the doorstep of the bakery, while inside, his father went on baking bread in the flickering shadows. Above the bakery the sky was always the same.

Long afterwards, the town learned that the blacksmith's son and the baker's wife were living in a city near the sea. Some said that they were happy; others said that they were not. The fruit dealer was of the latter opinion. Often he would give me a peach. On some days it was good, on others it was tasteless. . . .

translated by Merloyd Lawrence

Ethiopian Hunt

WAKENED BEFORE daybreak, in the darkness of my room, I used to hear the dogs howling at the hyenas that prowled the steep hillside, trying to come close to the village. I used to imagine them, still quite far off, silhouetted against the slope in the blue night light, silently advancing, then retreating, suddenly absorbed by shadows, while the dogs grew dizzy with barking, in the savage fraternity of beasts. Everything seemed enormous: the night, and the countryside, opening on to those expanses of moonlight and hyenas.

Sometimes I could hear the light, barefoot step of black men who smelled of musk. They wore *chamas*, that length of white cloth Ethiopians wrap round their naked bodies, which gives them the air of mummies suddenly called back to the world, getting on as best they can in their winding sheets. They passed close to the house, surrounded by barking, walking towards the hills swiftly and furtively, as if taking advantage of our sleep to cross this territory ordinarily closed to them, to which night gave them the keys.

Then morning came back with its rough rutted roads which one pulled towards oneself like an interminable anchor chain.

At that hour before the great heat bore down too heavily, when the air was clearer, and the jagged, bluish horizon seemed closer, when one felt encouraged, invited, to movement and liberty, one rediscovered the countryside, tortuous and barricaded, in which each step seemed weighted and chained, as in a dream.

There was, to begin with, the soil, as stony and deeply cut as a moraine. There were the grasses, long and pale, sometimes lying like cut swathes, or like rushes after a flood, sometimes standing upright, moving their meagre heads in a faint rustling which mingled with the buzzing of flies – dry, burning and agitated like tiny grains of black grass. There were thickets of dead thorn trees, bleached white by drought, and long close-grown stretches of dwarf trees with downy leaves: a thousand subtle prohibitions only gradually disclosed, creating a kind of discouragement for which one reproached oneself, as for a lack of ardour.

We would gladly have given in to our lassitude, and turned back, if, each morning when we were already far from the village, beginning to slow our pace and to feel our chains, there had not been a mass awakening of birds. I have never known such an abundance of species and variety of colour. There were African bustards, with yellow beaks and feet, black crowns and wing-tips fringed with white. There were *rhaads*, another kind of bustard, smaller, livelier, crested and more brilliantly coloured; francolins, with orange necklaces; *tetras*, which are large grouse; partridges, with red spots under their throats; blue pigeons, and still others. . . .

I didn't begin to know all their names and often confused them in their swift flights under the heavy foliage. One would catch in the shadows only a streak of colour which one couldn't place on the bird's body, summarized in a quick flash accompanied by an agitation of the air, as faint as the wind in the grass.

Then, on these still mornings, my companions would begin to fire, shooting at the birds who disguised themselves as they flew. Endless volleys shook the silence. It ceased to be a hunt and became an assault on the morning, blows struck against its closed doors, frantic efforts to penetrate its barricades of stones and pines and arrive at a world where, to begin with, birds had names.

We always finished by forcing our way in. Looking for the creatures we had killed, we no longer felt the restraining pull of grass and brush, the snares set for us by the land. We grew jolly, talked loudly, shouted to each other, while the sound of firing reverberated with an air, somehow, of joyous release, through the soft, discouraging mornings of hypocrite Ethiopia. I didn't like hunting, and never shot, myself. I discovered, however, that it held a key: the death of beasts.

The Greek innkeeper often acted as our guide. He was a man of fifty, threatened by death from angina pectoris. He rarely spoke, resembling in this most of his compatriots who lived in Ethiopia, in the boredom of isolated villages and the irritation of flies. And perhaps, too, he owed his habits of silence to hunting, for he excelled in this occupation. He knew all its seasons, and watched throughout the year its procession of furry harvests. Yes, harvests. On some days he killed as many as six boar, which his black servants would carry to the house. It made me think of laying up the season's produce in barns. A dead boar is like a shapeless vegetable mass, grey and lustreless, its long bristles matted with earth and blood.

I wondered why the Greek innkeeper killed so many. His family certainly couldn't eat them all, and the Ethiopians, servants and neighbours, despised this flesh, which is held to be pork by the Coptic religion and is forbidden. The dogs were allowed to gorge, and the rest was buried. The next day, the innkeeper returned to the hunt, silent, a cigarette between his lips, his face still drawn from a recent attack of angina, a man who carried death in his heart.

A day had not passed since we came to the village that he had not offered to take us hunting. He was urgent, and we allowed him to persuade us, but we could not see that his illness was getting worse. His wife, anxious and hostile, watched him leave. She was thin, wore black and held herself stiffly erect. Her dignity and self-possession seemed a kind of mourning.

The presence of the couple's only child, a girl of eighteen with a sombre, chiselled beauty, did not lighten the atmosphere of the house. Held by her parents in frightened subjection, Maria repressed the vitality of her age. She would have talked and laughed with us gladly had we been there during her free time, but hunting kept us away too often.

She reproached us for this, sometimes even shouting, when her father wasn't there, deploring that in his state of health he should insist upon these arduous marches through the forest, blaming us for abetting his passion. But since he would have indulged this passion whether or not he had company, I understood that this complaint was only a cover for the displeasure we caused by our absence.

Perhaps, too, she felt sympathy for our victims, the brilliantly coloured birds whose blood mingled with their feathers, as they lay with dangling heads on the edge of the table where we put them each evening when we came in. Like her mother, she looked at us each morning as we left with a kind of mute anger. I thought that since I carried no gun I might escape her censure. Then I thought that, to the contrary, she would probably see a cruel curiosity in the apparent gratuitousness of my participation. On the edge of the hunt and the cold pleasure of those who fired, was I not abandoning myself to a chase more subtle, amorous and perfidious, which consists of watching at length and describing the creatures who would die?

The Greek innkeeper took us to the forests where wild boar could be found. The jeep followed a deeply rutted road. Golden foxes, gazelles and hyenas with rheumy eyes fled through the bordering thickets. The animals pushed through the undergrowth towards those inaccessible places where, parcelled out as in a zoo, but animated with the constant agitation of animal liberty, there waited other gazelles, kudus, antelopes, monkeys and those invisible leopards who inhabited this country.

I liked to surprise these creatures and watch them take flight, in a terror so sudden it seemed to hang for an instant, suspended, as if painted against the thick growth of trembling bushes, with their bitter leaves. The Greek innkeeper told us that a little earlier in the year several hundred gazelles had assembled in a migration for which no one knew the reason. Their tightly grouped herd had moved through the brakes, crossed plateaus and valleys, at a steady regular pace. The creatures moved flank to flank, as if blinded by a dream. The innkeeper came right up to them and touched one with his hand. The animal didn't feel his touch; none of them even saw him. The rivers of gazelles washed gently against him, with a dry, musky odour. He didn't fire.

Now as he described the scene, he held his hand out before him; there, like water, a river of gazelles, breaking up further on, in the desert, in a great delta of silence. The world became once more a world of solitude and watchfulness.

The hunters opened the way for me, and I followed them across the grey forests. Those trees must never lose their leaves: the earth underneath them is bare and ashy between the trunks. The sun was hidden, the air still. I walked without sound, crumbling a leaf beneath my fingers. A boar ran out ahead of us. The Greek innkeeper fired, and the bullet raised a cloud of dust between the animal's legs. The creature staggered a few yards ahead of us, and then continued its course, one of its hind legs dangling. Suddenly it was evening.

We walked for hours through the still forest, and then moved into another forest. Each time we came to the edge of the trees, I imagined there would be strong light and laurels running down to the sea; but it was always a tufted, iron-grey valley separating us from the next forest. We crossed the valley, and unseen creatures fled into the thickness of the leaves.

One evening we wounded a boar mortally. There were no bullets left to finish him off. While we waited for his agony to end, the Greek innkeeper went back to get the truck for the carcass. It was already dark. A man whose face was no longer visible and I were left alone. At bay in a thicket, a shadow among shadows, the boar panted noisily. He was almost twice as large as our big European boar. We stood guard at a distance. In a sudden surge of life, he might attack us. Nevertheless, we had to be there. His final flight couldn't take him far, but far enough to lose him, if he tried it in our absence. The Greek innkeeper was slow in returning, and the boar was slow to die. When his breathing finally stopped, the silence was even worse; his agony had been company for us. I went slowly towards the thicket and struck a match. The animal's eyes were wide open, and he lay as he had been, ready to charge. His groin pressed against the earth, his neck bent under the weight of his head, he was less the image of death than of utter dejection.

The match burned itself out, and the night sent us back to our solitude. I thought I heard something rustle against the ground, and imagined scorpions, which the evening coolness brings out from under the stones. At last the truck came. We put the beast in the back. I sat beside it, my feet resting on the carcass, which filled the entire space. The spasmodic jerking of the truck communicated itself to that mass of still-warm flesh, and it seemed as if the animal were reviving. The night grew blacker. We could no longer distinguish the trees against the sky. A little later, close to the inn, we could see the glimmer of native fires. We pulled out the carcass and dumped it in a shed, which we locked because of hyenas. It was time to sleep. On the road, Ethiopians wrapped in their white *chamas* passed by, barefoot, silent, and vanished into the night. They never even looked at us. What could be happening in this country?

Sometimes I cursed it. Its somnolent indigence and filth, its feudal customs irritated me. But above all, its innocence. The tranquillity of the mornings, their transparent clarity, their flights of birds created a kind of well-being from which we were excluded, but whose mark the Ethiopians carried with their air of secrecy and mute pride. It was the first time I had seen our civilization as a demerit; and the silence of the country, its subtle austerities, constantly reminded us of it.

Every morning the Greek innkeeper appeared, his face paler and more drawn. His left arm was stiffening but he spoke of more distant excursions. He knew the surroundings of the village too well and suggested hunts for which we had to rise in darkness and drive for hours through a landscape of black mountains.

We crossed the Aouache and penetrated the territory of the Gallas, in the direction of Harrar. We already knew these people, as our village marked the boundary of their district and we feared them. Quite recently foreign travellers and Amharic Ethiopians had been emasculated. These criminal attacks were not expressions of vengeance. The Gallas were merely after virile trophies to bedeck themselves and insure their prestige in the eyes of their women. We were not enemies, but prey. We suppressed our fears: this menace was degrading. We were desired in a manner so precise and explicit that our male completeness became a kind of absurd virginity.

Our anxiety, and the silence of this district, less wooded and emptier, and the pallor of the earth and of the plants which grew in this light, as raw as in a premonition, made us feel that we were living in a dream.

There was a large brackish lake surrounded by a wide sterile zone which was flooded at certain seasons of the year and bleached white with mineral salts. Near the shore, the water which the clayey soil could not absorb filled any impression and after a few minutes coated the surface with a transparent jelly-like skin.

Pawprints pressed into this white mud were crisscrossed and superimposed, as if a hundred different creatures, friends or enemies, had trodden the same spot at the same moment: birds, cheetahs, hyenas, intermingled, united by night thirst, drawn by these waters, nitrous, gleaming, and dead under the moon.

Flights of flamingos swooped down into the unbearable glitter of the lake unruffled by any breeze, from which an occasional fish leapt and fell back, carving slow waves of mercury.

Close by was a smaller lake of sweet water, surrounded by trees and grasses of a sombre, violent green, against the white of the neighbouring shore: a kind of stagnant oasis. It was inhabited by crocodiles, who slid back into the water at our approach. We hid and soon their heads flowered against the surface. My companions fired. The crocodile disappeared, his eyes shot out, to die at the bottom of the lake, from which his body would rise after four days with its ringed tail and pale waxen stomach.

The hunters played this game on evenings after too rich a harvest had left them surfeited with the sickly sweet exhaustion of pleasure. They derived a certain glory from these exploits, which they described to Maria. She watched us fixedly, but her eyes turned most often to an Englishman in our group. Did she love him? But she had already gone into the next room. Silence fell again. My companions had not explained that they had fired on the crocodiles, on those gluey bubbles breathed up from the bottom when the shower of buckshot creased the black water of the lake, because it was essential to fire, to shake that insistent silence, to wake oneself from that dream where water froze in heat, where the beasts of creation, jostling in the fraternity of night, among them the hyenas with dogs' prints, came to drink at this lake, which was as bitter and pale as cold lye, and where in a depth of water darkened by rotting leaves crocodiles pushed to the surface with their blank, pupilless eyes. . . . It was essential to fire without stopping, to pound and crash against those doors. . . .

On our return journeys we often stopped at an isolated plantation owned by some Greeks. An avenue of papayas led up to the house.

One evening one of the planters asked the innkeeper: 'Do you have plenty of cartridges?'

The innkeeper answered that he had a substantial reserve. The capital was a day's journey. Its stores were often badly supplied. He had long ago taken his precautions. The planters were delighted: they needed munitions. Bands of *chiftas* – highwaymen along the main roads of Ethiopia – were roaming the district. They might find allies among the native workers the planters employed, who were dissatisfied with their lot. Thus, attacks with intent to rob might easily turn into an uprising.

The planters managed to infect us with their fears. We scrutinized the shadows on our homeward journeys. One evening in the middle of the road we found a bottle filled with a white liquid propped up as a support for a board which was lying on the ground. Some letters had been scrawled across it with black paint, not Amharic, but Latin characters: *Ambo*. This word had no meaning in any of the languages we knew. The place was absolutely deserted. Not so much as one car a week used this road. Who had left this curious message, and to whom was it addressed? Hares dashed across the road in the glare of our headlamps. My companions fired at them almost at random, again and again. It was the only way of answering that obscure message found by chance on the road. Its strangeness troubled us: not so much the unknown word, but the presence of this white bottle which in mid-desert made one think of a milkman's inadvertence and had the character of a demented invention.

I made a discovery: this country was mad. Not with a noisy and ecstatic madness, but a secret one, in the light and the silence. It soothed itself to sleep with incoherence, grew tortuous roads which lost themselves in forgotten landscapes where flies spun in circles, heaved up jagged mountains which slashed the dark horizon, weighted down its forests with soil of ash, spread out its leaden lakes in the thirst of noon and white prairies dry with hunger; only in its innumerable beasts could flashes of reality be found. In chasing them and shooting at them, the hunters were trying to re-establish, beginning at the most superficial level, some normal contact in this world given over to shapeless dreams, Hunting was an effort towards lucidity.

I wanted to explain this to Maria. She continued to look at us as we left with a face full of sadness and reproach. But she wouldn't have understood me. She was undoubtedly most anxious about her father's state of health. He had recovered quickly enough from his latest attack of angina, but his face held an expression of misery, a kind of spiritual suffering, as if, in his moments of respite, his sickness reached his soul, leaving behind not only the need for remedy, but also for consolation.

What consolation? I sensed that with his taste for authority, or for solitude, the innkeeper had long cut himself off from whatever consolation his wife or daughter might have brought him. His voice as he spoke to them never had the inflexion he had given it that day, when he described for us his river of gazelles. I could see him at that moment, holding out his hand to imaginary wild flanks with lustrous hides and sharply jutting bones. His hand trembled; no doubt because of his angina. But yet it is a blessing of such an illness that it makes the pounding of our heart discernible in our gestures.

Now, the innkeeper kept his silence, perhaps forever. I only caught him once, dreaming, immobile, holding his gun without firing. We had been walking north, and came to a stream that had overflowed its banks. There had been heavy rains. Migrating birds were landing there. Small black cranes were grouping themselves in the spindly trees like crows on a gallows. As they came down, they hung in the air, immobile, unfolding their long, dead legs, and making a slow vertical descent.

The light sank and lit only the brown waters. In the depths of the sky, in a tight formation which climbed like a column of smoke, and then spread out like a banner, unravelling and re-forming, thousands of sparrows were assembling for their next stage, which would open to them the Sudan, with its black cotton-seeds, the millet of the Nile valley and the burning glow of an endless summer. How isolated Ethiopia seemed, relegated to the shadows of the high country!

That evening we sat for a long time without talking. After a

few days my companions began to kill again. At night I heard
the hyenas walking close to the inn. The creatures we brought
back had left traces of their blood or scent on the ground. Mad
with fear and frustration the dogs barked at the walls. In the
house the two women were up, moving rapidly, speaking in
low voices. The innkeeper had suffered a new attack. He died
during the night to the howling of dogs.

They buried him in a little cemetery deeply shaded by
eucalyptus. My companions went back to their geological
work. We no longer had any taste for hunting. One day a
man from the plantation came in the greatest agitation. The
night before some natives had tried to approach near the farm
buildings. For three days they had noticed that the field hands
looked sullen and tried to avoid their masters. Everything
hinted at conspiracy, and the planters had come for the weapons
the innkeeper had stockpiled at the end of his life. Where were
they?

Maria and her mother were slow to answer, but the man
insisted: he would pay. Then the girl told him that when her
father died she had thrown all his munitions into the Aouache.
The planter swore at her, and left for the capital to look for
bullets. He also asked for police reinforcements.

He came back alone two days later supplied with munitions
and assured by the administration that a truck-load of soldiers
would be sent without fail. It was already too late. During the
night that followed his visit to the inn, two outbuildings had
been burned. There had been shooting, but because of the
inadequate supply of bullets the Greeks' defence had been
feeble, and one of their men was wounded.

The planters came to the inn, and their companion joined
them there on his return from the capital. They were pale
with anger. Maria hid. They left with expressions of hatred,
and their resentment did not weaken in the days that
followed.

In due course, the group I was accompanying was called
into another district and had to leave the village. The young

girl who had not wept at her father's death came to say goodbye with red eyes. Several months went by. When by chance
we came back through the village Maria had already been
missing for some weeks. She had gone to walk beside the
Aouache. They began to search at nightfall, but every effort
proved vain. There were the river current and crocodiles, and
on land, hyenas and vultures who came down from the trees
with the air whistling through their great grey wings.

I chased away those images. There were also the Ethiopian
mornings given up to silence. And there were the birds, diverse
and colourful, pursuing their flight above all death: bustards,
rhaads, francolins, partridges, pigeons and many others
whose names I never knew.

translated by Lily Emmet

The Watershed

S HE WOULD not have been able to say what it was that obsessed her about that sound, repeated almost every evening, of someone swimming in the darkness.

Whether to avoid attracting insects, or because it seemed wasteful to use the electricity for one person, or because the swimmer himself preferred the shadows, the lights around the pool were not turned on. Her ignorance about the real reason for this, and the perfectly valid nature of all three hypotheses, heightened the impression of absurdity which came over MCH whenever she listened to the nocturnal splashing.

The same ambiguity of cause and effect appeared again and again in the everyday life of this country, in the daily spectacle of the streets of Manila, giving rise to erratic fancies and tendentious opinions. A few questions might have solved everything. But there was neither the time nor the opportunity.

Drawn towards an explanation which would best justify her annoyance, MCH thought that the solitary swimmer chose the night in order to hide some physical defect, or to make sure that his forbidden recreation was kept a secret. No doubt it was an employee of the Club, or a Filipino servant, a cook with a shiny, emaciated body, taking his revenge in the shadows.

MCH was entirely without racial or social prejudices and would have been only too delighted to find that a native was illicitly enjoying the pool, had he done so with more discretion. But this endless diving, kicking, snorting, only went to show how these people take advantage of any freedom they are given. Through the glass doors of the nearly empty dining room of the Navy Club, left partly open in order to moderate the chill of excessive air conditioning, one could hear first a noisy plunge, then a rather long silence, followed by furious strokes through the water and finally a kind of trickling sound.

The shadows seemed to increase the resonance of the water, its weight, its resistance to the human body, even its dimensions. By day so limpid and calm, by night the pool seethed with laboured, noisy struggles, as though a man were being saved from drowning. His survival each time was uncertain, undeserved, for the man (it was a man; now and then MCH could make out a vague silhouette) returned again and again to the diving board, hesitating before he plunged, prolonging the suspense, his body finally hitting the water with a more resounding impact than ever.

At this exact moment, MCH would imagine, or more precisely, would see the man's body, in its nakedness, before it was swallowed up by the water – the sullen nakedness of someone who is alone. Perhaps 'sullen' was not the right word. But what kind of expression, other than one which expressed ill-humour, could define the feeling of dismal continuation, of physical numbness, which came to MCH every morning when she surveyed her own body in the bathroom mirror? She dressed quickly, to escape herself, to make herself vanish: a kind of plunge into the anonymity or the disguise of clothes. ... But was this enough to justify a comparison between herself and the relentless diver? The man was probably training for an athletic competition. And on second thought, he was more likely an American, or a European; a Filipino would never have shown such perseverance.

Of course the simplest solution would have been to go out the dining room door and take a look, instead of dwelling on this trivial mystery. MCH had thought of this, but soon realized that such a move was riskier than it appeared. Beyond the thin band of light which ran along outside the glass wall of the dining room, beneath the sky laden with typhoon clouds, there was total darkness. In order to see the man's face MCH would have to wait until he came out of the water, and go up close to him – a rather forward act, one which would give the wrong impression, invite familiarity, or even . . .

Even what? It was then that she discovered, within herself, an anxiety quite out of proportion to this prospect of an encounter, at night, beside the pool. Beyond all the thoughts aroused by the image of a Filipino servant violating the Club rules and revelling in the pool like a boisterous child, or the image of an American or a European, shivering with loneliness, in spite of the ninety-degree heat, there lay, as MCH was forced to admit, a more imminent threat: a cruel, dangerous presence, very close by, the presence of a being who was ill-defined but capable, through his ferocious efforts in the water and the darkness, of summoning forth the truth hidden behind the peaceful, everyday façade of this country.

To begin with the most obvious facts, with geographical reality, water was the truth of this country. More than a thousand islands and, in each one of them, overflowing rivers, the network of *arroyos* irrigating the rice fields, swamps hidden beneath stiff, fleshy vegetation, ditches of stagnant water along village streets. All around, the grey lustre of the sea. And on top of all this, for two months of the year, the monsoon season, when the earth siphons away the sky. Water everywhere, but not just any kind of water: water rich in amoebae, bilharzia larvae, leeches, snakes, and here and there a half-submerged tree trunk which turns out to be a sleeping crocodile.

Local colour. The opaque surface of rivers murky with silt, of lagoons green as the wide, overhanging leaves of the tropical yam which rose along the edge, suggested dangers which were attractive because, without them, one would not have felt the full excitement of being in a strange land. In addition to the picturesque zoology, or more accurately, bacteriology, there was also 'historical colour'. At the end of the war, before surrendering, the Japanese had dumped tons of weapons and ammunition into the rivers and water holes. The Americans, once they were victorious, had imitated them, finding it pointless to load used supplies and excess shells and grenades back into their ships. And so, around the islands where sharks roamed, remembering the khaki dead of Corregidor, a sunken arsenal had taken shape, rising here and there into velvety grey heaps explored by divers.

Actually, only the Filipinos dove, and among them, only the poorer classes. Accustomed, from a very early age, to a lack of sanitation, they had more or less acquired a natural immunity to the parasitic diseases carried by the water. The snakes and crocodiles were not a real danger to them; the Malaysian litheness of their lean bodies had been modelled for millenniums after reptiles, and the surprises of the water. There were still the submerged explosives. They dove for them, brought them up on the banks to sell. Once in a while, upstream, or down, an explosion was heard. But the profits were worth the risk.

For the poor, the water, was still posssible, almost benign. They enjoyed its coolness at the height of a suffocating day. From the window of her office which overlooked a canal, MCH would see men and girls swimming, sometimes holding a little sprig between their teeth, from an aromatic plant whose name she had once heard. When they came out of the water, and sat down on the banks, the flimsy cotton of their tight bathing suits clung to them and left nothing of their sex to the imagination. A boy would lay a hand on a girl's thigh and perhaps they would make love then and there, in the mud, mixing their amoebae, coupling together until they attained the blind, moist complicity of larvae.

For MCH, who was perspiring beneath her white coat, this scene held a terrifying power of attraction. She imagined the coolness of the water, the smoothness of the silt banks, the fragrance of the leafy sprig which the boys held in their mouths, in a swarm of flies, to be sure, and with the little black snails of bilharzia sticking to the grass, a rim of pale worms at the water's edge, but why should desire (the fragrance of the sprig) be isolated from the rest of this great biological playground, this teeming mortality?

Aside from the political and metaphysical conflicts which came between them and the people of this country, the Americans and the other Occidentals were set apart because they found the water sinful. Not just unhealthy – this word did not carry the full strength of their taboo – it was 'sinful'. And it was everywhere. It was the only source of fertility, the only promise of refreshment, of physical happiness. A small amount had been cautiously isolated and neutralized, to fill the blue tile swimming pool of the Club. Really neutralized? The doctors were dubious; the coarse filters, the antiseptics diluted into too weak a solution, were a precarious defence against the microscopic parasites. They still pullulated behind a mask of transparency.

Therefore, abstain, as much as possible. But for whose sake? For the sake of one's own health, naturally, but also for the public health, for the well-being of society, for economic development, and, in the long run, for the future of democracy, since, as everyone knows, disease leads to subversion. And finally, for the sake of God. One thing led to another, inexorably, and MCH, in the Club dining room, listening to the water lapping in the pool, in this whole aquatic country, could imagine that she heard the clamour of Hell.

And so, in this yearning for physical abandon, for slime, for risks accepted in a kind of carefree inertia, she rediscovered Hell. Not as she had known it at home, in the United States, abstract, artificial, but as a part of nature. It was not surprising that, for a people who were still in childhood, God should let Evil survive as the most tangible of realities.

MCH had not, however, anticipated any of this when she agreed to go to the Philippines. She had imagined that she would be clothing herself in virtue, or at least in the wisdom, the enlightened charity offered by the international health organization which she was joining. It was not the missionary spirit, the quinine pill followed by a communion wafer, the redeeming hypodermic, no, a rational, scientific approach, a kind of Five-Year-Plan for public health linked to economic redevelopment and cultural evolution; there were pages and pages written on the subject. . . .

Water was not mentioned, or when it was, it was water which had been thoroughly analysed, seen through the misty transparency of a test tube, not this green, or silt-laden water, flowing or stagnating between overgrown banks, cool beneath the oppression of day, in which nearly naked boys and girls swam about with upturned chins, holding their smiles high – the water which lay waiting for MCH.

MCH, known to some as Clara: one and the same woman. The initials, which were those of her speciality (Mothers' and Children's Health) had become her surname. 'Emceeaych.' The name had ironic overtones. Clara had a full-blown kind of beauty which, at first glance, made her seem the embodiment of maternity. Traces of childhood on her face, a suggestion of dimples, clear eyes to which fluttering lids now and then gave a note of surprise, tempered this solemn impression of a maternal calling, and almost made one think that behind the façade of medicine, Clara MCH still clung to little girl's games. All this, however, was not without ambiguity, and to Clara, more than ever, the problems of gynaecology and lactation seemed to stem from the awesome and dismaying sexual impregnation of the world.

She had felt at an early age that her physical make-up, her childish, vulnerable, and at the same time generous nature, drew her towards passivity in love, towards that greedy, self-abandonment which, despite the wilful perversity of pleasure, allows biological determination to triumph. She had discovered that, unless she was careful, love, in spite of appearances to the contrary, would come her way only through rape and child-birth.

In choosing as her speciality, at the end of her medical studies, problems of maternal and infant health, she had sought to dominate these inclinations, to acquire a scientific impartiality, and, by dint of cold, sober practice, to unmask, to stifle the secret longing for abandon which probably still lay hidden within her. This attempt at self-liberation had not brought the results she expected. A theorist, she had also become doctrinaire, and confined within the strict principles she expounded, as far as her personal life was concerned she could only abstain, rather like the nuns who often served in the same profession as she. To escape, she would have to break with the order completely, for, in the last analysis, everything was bound up together: the biological and social condition of women, economic and scientific rationalism, the American Way of Life, civilization. There was no freedom, no real freedom except on the outside, in this somewhat putrid, magical universe in which water was the principal element, or in any case, the symbol.

Clara had enough insight into the workings of the mind to know that anxiety, interior conflicts, are always touched off or reinforced by the appearance of a symbol. Nature begins to take on greater significance than it should, assuming that equilibrium, peace of mind are dependent in this world on the existence of a certain amount of silence, of meaninglessness. But was it a question of mental equilibrium, or of the larger order of things? Clara was aware that, from a logical point of view, the fascination which the water held for her had something abnormal about it, as did the temptation and, already, the remorse which she discovered in the noise from the pool. Nevertheless, she asked herself whether this 'clairvoyance', or more precisely, this 'voice' which came to her, rather than warning of neurotic troubles, did not herald the approach of truth.

Of course it is characteristic of neuroses to simulate extreme lucidity. For this reason, a diagnosis could only lead her to dismiss her own reasoning, and to condemn her leanings towards a seductive but unfortunate form of logic.

Where were the others, with all their healthy logic? The others? They were honouring the contract they had signed. Belonging to the American army, the administration, or international organizations, they had accepted, unconditionally, to serve in this country for two years. Most of them set about their duties with great seriousness, not only a desire to be promoted, but also an attempt to learn, to understand. They forgot, however, that one does not understand with one's head, but with one's whole destiny. They did not intend these two years to be part of their destiny, but only a chapter in their professional careers, illustrated with exotic memories.

To be sure, these people wished to participate as much as possible in the life of the country, but they drew the line at passion, and above all, at sin. He who is without sin remains an outsider. There they were, foreigners ('But I am still a foreigner, too!') behind the glass windows of a cabin cruiser, navigating the endless watery stretches of these islands, making observations, and more observations, and passing various precision instruments back and forth.

Among the Americans and other foreigners, such instruments were of the utmost importance; they explored the country with one eye glued to a microscope. The Occident surveyed the Philippines with relentless myopia. Clara, too, examined the slides, but beyond the little radius of brightness where the spirochetes of yaws or malarial parasites were held transfixed, other realities, more or less disturbing, swam before her eyes, like those which distract a horse without blinkers, and surround him, though one rarely realizes this, with a real universe of dreams.

The others did not see beyond their slides. Every evening,

one of Clara's colleagues, a Bolivian doctor, put a mule in a cage of coarse wire netting, in order to attract mosquitoes. He could thus record the hours at which the insects were most active, capture a good number, and do autopsies which established the proportion of disease carriers among them. To allow the mosquito (*Anopheles*) to settle on him in peace, the animal's legs and tail were tied.

Clara saw the mule; she could not stop seeing the mule, held motionless in this kind of birdcage, eaten alive, especially around the groin, blinking his eyelids. A symbol, there again: For after all, Clara asked herself, what do they want from me, all these rational men? The evening is the hour for mosquitoes, also the hour when all those eyes are laid upon me. . . .

The comparison with the mule was exaggerated, whimsical, of course; though when night fell, and all one could see of the captive mule was his belly, the almost hairless parts near the joining of the thighs, soft as chamois . . . Clara probably appeared to the men, with their shadowy desires in some such way as this. Once again the attraction of rape, of forced procreation: 'Someone should get her pregnant, that's what she needs,' said an Israeli public health officer (Hungarian, originally) in charge of setting up a 'programme' for the city of Manila.

Though he did not realize it, Clara had heard him. And so they were all agreed on one point: they wanted her to grow up, to become a woman, and at the same time, with an even more acute pleasure which they did not admit, they wanted to stifle the little girl in her. . . . The little girl got on their nerves, in every sense of the word. In the bar, or in the Club dining room, they would joke, with a kind of tight-lipped indulgence or sly superiority, about Clara MCH's innovations.

They had just discovered that she had used a pictorial language to instruct the Filipino midwives, who, due to the lack of medical personnel, continued to preside at childbirth under the remote supervision of the Maternal Health service directed by Clara. Like the majority of the population, these

good women, with expert hands but heads stuffed with superstitions, were illiterate. In the interior, people could write only
their names. They learned this from the priest who, at the
occasion of first communion, felt obliged to provide each of his
neophytes with a little temporal passport.

In order to keep check, for post-natal visits, as they said in
medical jargon, Clara had asked the midwives to fill out small
forms in pictures for each newborn baby. A circle, bisected by
a line which showed only at the circumference, indicated a boy.
'Why not two circles side by side?' cried the Israeli, laughing.
A girl was indicated by the same little circle but with two wings.
Clara had grown to regret her choices; she had made up the
code very quickly and used the first ideas that came into her
mind.

The others in the group had found this seraphic little symbol
of femininity were amusing. The British doctor who had come
to this country to do a study of the relationship between mental
health and economic under-development had interpreted it as
an interesting bit of self-revelation, proof that Clara 'idealized'
the feminine condition and fled the realities of sex.

Clara had defended herself. Did they by any chance think
that she was a virgin? Of course not, but just the same . . . Clara
had suddenly felt the faces of the three or four men leering at
her with a kind of appetite. But she had not let it bother her.
She would never give in to them.

One of them who was neither a doctor nor a sociologist, a
naval attaché with the American embassy, young, blond, and
wearing a white uniform, eventually stood up for Clara. These
little pictures had a poetic charm about them, and were reminis-
cent of primitive ideograms, a universal language! So was the
little sun next to the day of the month when the birth occurred
(Clara had distributed loose-leaf calendars to the midwives). . . .

In arguing with so much conviction, the naval attaché
thought he was being quite clever. He had been courting Clara
for two months. Hoping to attract her attention, he was
collecting local legends, in which he hadn't the faintest interest,

burdening his mind with *aswangs*, the local black or white spirits (they often changed colour which did not simplify matters) who lived in the trees. He served this up to Clara with elo-quence that was laboured, but most commendable in a baseball player.

Clara found this folklore and superstition very tiresome. The quality she found attractive and, at the same time, frightening in this country was its primordial freedom, and the sense of doom which came with it. By a return to the elements, or to an elementary level of existence, and exposing herself to the dangers inherent in it, she would free herself from the rules of the game. To be both a doctor and a citizen of the United States meant that she was caught in an ethic which dictated the feminine part of her destiny in no uncertain terms: submis-sion, more or less disguised or adapted to the desires of men, the biological consequences of love, a certain emotional and social outlook, etc. One thing led to another. The order ad-mitted no deviations. Madness was the only escape, for how could one even consider such sorry recourses as eroticism or alcohol?

Here one could 'take the plunge'. (The expression took on its full literal and symbolic meaning.) A deep plunge. How deep? Back to one's origins? This was a word to avoid; it suggested a natural order. For there was no natural order; there was no such thing as a purpose in life. In the early societies (but why speak of societies when tribal organization was already a form of sclerosis?) nothing was fixed; nothing was established: matriarchy or patriarchy, human sacrifice, polygamy, incest; even the perpetuation of the species occurred by chance amidst epidemics, disasters and murder; life was a haphazard after-math of death. . . . That was freedom, the only real freedom, the kind one attains through despair.

How could Clara achieve this, assuming she was able to overcome her fears? Perhaps by mingling with the people. Through corruption, they are returning to a state of amorality no doubt rather similar to that which they had known at the beginning of time. First believing in a kind of animism, then thrown into the Catholicism of their first invaders, then influenced by an Americanism interrupted by a brief period of Nipponese militarism, finally surrendered to a false independence characterized by the childish artifacts of a civilization of imports, disoriented, literally 'broken', the only way they could assert themselves was through a wild license not unlike their savage origins. They played truant, bursting with childishness and perversity. Brown-skinned adolescents swam in the polluted waters, chewing on a twig, blood brothers of the reptiles, born yesterday out of the clay banks where Coca-Cola bottles lay scattered and where now and then a transistor radio – stolen no doubt – broadcast an American song.

Would Clara ever be able to know this truth, this dark, buried truth which continued to exist in spite of the hazards of progress? Trying to look at things in the simplest, most concrete form, she sometimes said to herself that she should fall in love with a Filipino, or more precisely, should sleep with one. But her profession froze all the ordinary people who came near her. And besides, could she really conceive of such a thing? . . . These men, often handsome, but who never brushed their teeth, rarely washed, whose bellies were too hollow, whose penises were pointed, rather like that of a dog. . . . There, she was balking already. And yet, on the other side, what a promise of deep waters!

As for the middle-class Filipinos, everything about them was bland. Well fed, they poured forth unctuous civilities, in English. They invited Clara to evening parties where they served suckling pig on a spit. The wives of these local officials had their pet charities, foundling homes and nurseries, in which Clara was sometimes obliged to participate. No matter how she clung to the rigid scientific principles and the long view of the international organization which she represented, she found herself slipping, again and again, into charity, hand to mouth assistance, hit or miss compassion. The guilt she felt about this became even more acute at fashionable receptions where it was tacitly agreed upon to leave infant mortality in the cloakroom. The Filipino ladies, though readers of *Harper's Bazaar*, clung to a native flavour in their elegance. They wore bodices of stiff tulle in pale colours, with sleeves that flared out at the shoulders, rather like wings. . . .

Of course! This was what had come into Clara's mind when she was trying to think of a symbol for a baby girl, in the birth certificates to be used by the midwives! Why hadn't she remembered earlier? She felt a real sense of relief when she discovered that this ideogram did not reveal any latent desires in her, any secret conflicts, only an unwitting fantasy of memory. The British doctor had been wrong; she was no different from any of the others in the group, more intelligent, more sensitive, perhaps, but essentially their fellow creature.

When she remembered this she left the dining room (the lone swimmer was still diving in the pool but that was another story) and went to find the Englishman. He was in the bar, in the company of the Bolivian, a Frenchwoman from UNESCO, the naval attaché and the Israeli. She was smiling. (Later on she probably wondered why; her sudden intrusion into the bar was ridiculous.) Interrupting the conversation, she explained almost breathlessly about this image which had come back to her: the wings. . . .

The others looked at her, surprised. What was she talking about? Oh, yes. . . . They remained glum. An oppressive evening. Sometimes they seemed to be exasperated by Clara. The Englishman, the Bolivian, and the Israeli were married. They knew she could never become their mistress, even if she consented: too many complications. Their desire turned in circles and grew weary.

'My dear, you certainly take yourself seriously, don't you?' the Englishman said finally, trying to smile.

She soon left and went to join the two head nurses, also American, white, insipid, with whom she shared a table in the dining room. The others were right; she was different. It hardly mattered that they misunderstood her, that they saw as childish self-centredness what, in fact, was her insight into another world than theirs, a world into which she had not yet quite dared to escape, but which nevertheless, she should not reject.

She had lied to herself. The wings she had chosen as a symbol of femininity were not a reflection of the native dress. This was just a trivial coincidence. The Englishman's psychoanalytic interpretation was equally worthless. The meaning behind the little wings lay somewhere else entirely. Someday Clara would learn more. The others would never understand.

She was thus gradually discovering the pride of loneliness, that vague expectancy directed only upon oneself. She discovered the reverent self-respect which grows out of the misunderstanding and indifference of others. She discovered how a frustrated need for revenge turns into a kind of inward obstinacy. From then on, she imperceptibly and almost unwittingly emphasized the qualities in her behaviour which alienated her from others. She dismissed the naval attaché with cruel abruptness, sending him off to the prostitutes of Cavite (a large American military base outside of Manila), and gave in wholly to her imagination.

Multiplying the number of inspection tours she took across the country, she tried to come face to face with the landscape, the people, their evil spirits who seemed to her the key to freedom. Nevertheless she was unhappy. She would have liked to sleep in a hut now and then, to wake up soiled by the dank earth beneath the bamboo walls, to run down to the river, or wade half-engulfed in a rice field, towards a man who was also submerged up to his thighs, his bare chest reflecting the gold of the water.

To distract herself from these strange dreams and her loneliness, she went about her work with a joyful zeal which, she admitted to herself, was somewhat in defiance of the others, those complacent theoreticians with their two-year contracts. Continuing her instruction of the native midwives, teaching them the secret of sterilizing instruments before delivery, she conceived a method by which these women, who had no watches and, besides, could not read them, would be able to measure time. The water in which the instruments were plunged had to be kept boiling for a certain number of minutes. Clara made up a song, which, if begun just as the water started to boil, would not be over until the aseptic process was complete.

The song, really a little counting rhyme, mingled Tagalog expressions – those that Clara knew – with the pidgin-English of the midwives. The words were obscure and perfectly non-sensical. But this was precisely what would appeal to the love of magic and ritual in these toothless old women. Clara had of course personified the water, in her little obstetrical ditty, and without paying much attention, had made it masculine: 'Mister Water'. She had not dared to call it 'Lord Water'. In the song, it swelled, trying to imitate the sea, killed the vicious serpents who whistled as it began to boil, but obviously none of this had any meaning. The sex of the water, even the idea of the song, were all quite meaningless. Nothing mattered. Except the hut, the dank earth, the rice fields, the rice fields through which she would walk.

Clara came back to Manila every evening, worn out from riding in the jeep, driven by a silent little chauffeur with black lips, and went to dine at the Club, first ordering a whisky, a habit she had resumed. It was just at this moment, one evening, that they all came over to her, smiling. They were all in a good mood, apparently, What had happened? The Israeli always spoke first. The little song. Come now. They were all dying to hear it. While on a tour of inspection in the villages, they had been told about it.

Clara sensed that this was a planned attack. Standing slightly behind the rest, the English doctor had a serious, inquisitive expression on his face. A report to administration headquarters, a leave of absence due to nervous depression, and a trip home were but a step away. Clara chose to react cheerfully but she suddenly realized that it would be hard to omit the elements in the song which echoed, to a certain extent, the old superstitions and quackery. This would be the basis for the criticism, as yet unformulated, which she could read in the virulent smiles of those around her. To be sure, it was part of the strategy of both the American administration and the international organization to respect local traditions, in other words to let them wither gradually. But that was a far cry from substituting new superstitions! This would renew the hold of Evil and ignorance, when the very purpose of their mission was to heal, to bring the light.

Clara defended herself, trying to laugh. The amusing thing about this song was its lack, deliberate of course, of any meaning whatsoever: the same principle as a child's counting rhyme, a way of singing away the minutes, with a catchy rhythm which checked the impatience of the old women. . . .

'Well then, let's hear it!'

Clara began to panic. Why sing this nonsense? Its purpose was hygienic, not aesthetic. It was ridiculous to keep after her in this way. In the first place none of them knew a single word of Tagalog. The Bolivian protested: oh yes! The proof was that he understood the first verse perfectly – unfortunately the only one the people in the villages could remember. He recited the verse, emphasizing each word: 'The fish who swallowed the river was caught . . .' This was promising. Wouldn't she please sing the rest?

Clara looked around, hoping for a way out.

'I can't. We're not alone.'

They turned round. She was right. He had just come in and was ordering a drink at the bar. His hair was still wet. Even without this, Clara would have recognized him as the man who took possession of the pool every night. The shape of his body, perhaps, his torso, a slightly too exaggerated trapezoid. . . . Suddenly she was no longer afraid of the others. She had been dreaming; she had sought to sublimate, in the search for some obscure aquatic legend, some bit of pagan wisdom, the very natural desire which this naked man, seen vaguely through the dining room windows, had aroused in her. One lone man, naked in the darkness, at the end of the diving board, contemplating his plunge with the almost painful concentration men sometimes show in love. . . . It was all so marvellously simple!

The serenity which came to her all at once, as she realized what lay behind her distraught mood during the last few weeks, seemed to disarm the others. They no longer had before them a guilty child, who had strayed into an adult world, but a woman who was entirely sure of herself, lecturing them on the basic instruction of native health workers and the value of poetry, no matter how superficial, in what was called 'the psychological approach'. They did not let her convince them, but, by upholding opposing theories, they allowed room for discussion, while earlier they had been seeking only evidence to use against Clara, proof that her mind was deranged. The man at the bar had finished his drink and gone out. A few days later when he met Clara, and had an opportunity to talk to her, he admitted having been slightly disappointed that evening.

For the last two weeks he had seen her through the windows of the Club dining room every time he came out of the water. She could not see him, for he stood in the shadows, and that was what made his glimpse of her all the more revealing. Clara sat in profile, with the head nurse on her left. The other nurse was opposite her colleague. Clara had no one in front of her and could look straight ahead into the dining room which was well lit but three-quarters empty. Nothing is more moving than to catch another human being off guard, in this state of immobility, staring into space with an almost imperceptible forward thrust of his or her face, as though waiting for a signal from an object or a person a great distance away, but knowing very well that, once again, nothing will happen.

Besides, most of the time there is neither an object nor a person to answer this appeal. There was nothing in front of Clara. The young woman did not even seem aware of what lay before her eyes. Her mind, her glance, were vacant, vacant of everything but this vague hope. But the word 'hope', with all its sentimental associations, its stereotyped connotation of a bright light looming ahead, was not really appropriate. In her mind was rather that piercing note which continues to ring even when the rest of one's being is utterly silent, when thoughts are still unformed: a relentless solicitation.

In her face could be read that state of purity which sometimes arises out of stillness and solitude. Clara's expression, the intensity of her stare (sometimes the man came close enough to be able to make out the light circles around her eyes, the kind which suggest a faraway silence) became a summons, the one which is heard in every human being, in moments like this, and which sooner or later the whole world must answer.

The solitary swimmer had gradually become attached to this face which reappeared in the same spot every evening, enticing him with silence. It had almost been an unpleasant surprise to him to hear Clara talking so loudly and forcefully when he had come into the bar. Usually he never set foot there. That evening he had wanted to get rid of the stale taste which the water in the pool had left in his mouth. A typhoon was probably on its way, for then the water seemed to grow heavier, to exude the slightly sweet miasma of the marshes. It was a kind of awakening, one might think, like the seasonal phenomena which stir living organisms from within, subjecting them to the rhythms of mating, of ovulation. Even matter was animated, at least in this country where the heat aroused the most inert elements, imbuing them with an expectancy, a nameless desire, so that they were akin in a certain sense to Clara, leaning slightly forward and waiting in the deserted silence of the dining room. It curved them inwardly into tongues of fire.

Water into fire. Eventually it led to this, to a fusing of opposites, as in the ancient lore of alchemy.

The man who swam in the pool had not gone so far as this. He had told Clara simply that he had seen her, day-dreaming, in profile, through the window, and that 'she spoke to him'. He had also said that he had come into the bar that evening because

7

of the unbearably fetid taste of the water. 'This happens whenever a typhoon is on the way.' Clara had filled in the rest. Everything was starting all over again. Why flee, why lie to herself, why blame everything on the normal desires aroused in a single woman, desires almost anatomical in detail, foreseen, matter of course, and to a certain extent, bourgeois? Why not admit that she was drawing close to the strange 'realm'. 'The fish who swallowed the river was caught . . .' A coincidence (but beware of looking too closely at coincidences!) had brought the swimmer into the bar, with his wet hair, just at the moment when the Bolivian doctor was reciting the first verse of that absurd little ditty for midwives. . . . 'I am losing my mind,' Clara said to herself, as she talked to the man and felt the direction in which her thoughts were slipping.

They met at a reception at the Embassy, a tedious affair which it would have been impolite and awkward not to attend. When the man – his name was John, Clara had not caught the rest when they were introduced – moved away, after having chatted with her at length, Clara made some inquiries. One of the foreign service officers told her what she wanted to know. John V had married the daughter of M, one of the representatives of a Pittsburg metallurgical firm. He was here in the Philippines to set up some kind of copper refinery. He also seemed to be interested in salvaging military supplies. . . . 'A dreamer, as you can see. . . .' Clara did not bother to smile or to discreetly question the judgement of this civil servant who was known for the mediocrity of his intellect.

Justified or not, the opinions of others concerning the lone swimmer were quite indifferent to her. Her feelings towards him were divorced from all social or intellectual, if not from all human, values. What she looked forward to vaguely in their meeting, and from those that followed, was a kind of transmutation, a future of successive metamorphoses, which would carry her into a new domain, a domain where love (if one could still speak of it at all) would be identical with the freedom and silence of lizards, of reptiles.

She was thus delighted that John V had not tried to court her in any obvious way. He had mentioned only the mute rapport which had arisen between them, through the glass windows of the dining room, an observation which might have seemed like the most hackneyed romanticism, the usual 'line' in fact, if, as he spoke of this first contact between them, he had not appeared preoccupied, even annoyed. He seemed like someone who is suddenly faced with an unexpected predicament, saddled with unwanted responsibilities, or more precisely, with a shipwreck companion. There was nothing, however, in his attitude which betrayed a feeling of superiority or a conscious effort to step, then and there, into the role of protector. There was only the surprise, not unlike vexation, of finding his own destiny linked irrevocably with that of someone else.

And so it seemed the most natural thing in the world when John, not with any great eagerness, but as though he were soberly fulfilling an obligation, set about seeing Clara again. This took place at the Navy Club, in the presence of others in the group who felt disposed to adopt the new arrival. They did not realize right away that he had come to see Clara. Thinking that he was disoriented in a new country, and sought companionship or advice from them, they undertook, with a certain enthusiasm, to facilitate what they called his 'adaptation'. At first they were puzzled by his silence, but soon interpreted it as the shyness an ordinary businessman might feel in the presence of scientific experts.

Even though it only confirmed her expectations, Clara was impressed by John's quietness, and the serenity it conveyed. Without succumbing again to fanciful dreams (Clara had kept her imagination in check for several days now), she could say to herself that John was there as a man who has come to take delivery of something, and is asked to be patient a moment. But Clara was not stalling. She was very attentive to him, remaining constantly by his side, trying to make him talk more. What was he waiting for? Why didn't he take her away.

This was not the impatience of a woman in love. Clara was

no longer sure that she desired John. She knew only that they would leave together, and her anticipation was turning into uneasiness, anxiety.

Soon enough, however, her pursuit of the newcomer became obvious to the others. They were deeply shocked. To them it was evidence of unbridled eroticism, a pathological symptom which could be traced directly to the contaminated atmosphere, the deranged and at the same time depraved condition of the whole country, of the inorganic elements, the animal and vegetable kingdom, as well as of the human population, the throngs of brown, fever-prone bodies. . . . They were not against love, on the contrary, they encouraged it, but only within certain categories, on the one hand, the framework of biology, morality, and an up-to-date social system, and on the other (extramarital affairs, for instance), the realm of lust, relief of psychological tension, or discreet, sophisticated recreation. Outside of these definitions and categories, there was only disease and anarchy.

Their indignation was also directed at John, who was directly responsible for the shocking conduct of Clara MCH. He had capitalized, they thought, on his silence, his air of mystery. Not bad, for a scrap metal dealer. They avoided him and began to stay away from the Club. Clara and John found themselves alone.

John did not seem so delighted at this as Clara had expected. For a moment she felt great uncertainty. What if she had been mistaken? What if, in spite of all her premonitions, this man had lingered to chat with her at the Embassy, only in search of an escape from loneliness and a way of joining the little group whose animated conversations he could follow through the window next to the pool?

Since the city was then celebrating a season of Catholic holidays, and they had to find some way to amuse themselves, John took Clara away from the empty Club, on walks which soon became exhausting. One of them led along a bare esplanade in the port, above the docks, at the end of which lay the prison where Rizal, the hero of Philippine independence, was held captive and executed. John seemed fascinated by this lonely, sun-scorched spot. He went as close as possible to the edge. Far below, the murky water, iridescent with oil slick, lapped against the hulls of forgotten ships.

One day he explained to Clara that to him this was the real point of no return. Going from island to island, through the rest of the Philippines, one could feel a sense of progression, of hope. But this spot, on the shore of Luzon, the northernmost island, was a land's end, with only the seas beyond. Of course ships left every week, and planes left for the United States almost every evening. You could easily go aboard. But they were not leaving at that very moment, that moment when you give a sudden start, when you are seized by anguish, by a childish panic that makes you want to close your eyes with all your might, when you desire so desperately to leave. It was possible to leave, of course, but preparations were necessary, arrangements, and above all reason and reflection. There was the risk of changing one's mind. Leaving should be as easy as shouting.

Clara listened. She asked no questions. In time, the man would explain everything. Clara already recognized the sense of urgency to which he alluded, as he leaned over the oil-streaked water where rusty steamships lay at anchor, that blind, insane longing, for she felt it within herself. The object of her longing was different, for she had no thought of leaving yet. But this was unimportant. The only thing that mattered was the power of their desires, their irrational impulses which revealed a need for complete freedom.

One evening, on their way back, as they passed close to the prison where Rizal had been held, John made a vague gesture towards the spot where he had been executed.

'I almost died in the Philippines, myself.'

He had fought the Japanese, at Leyte. Clara nodded, more out of politeness than real feeling: oh yes, the war. . . . John pointed his thumb over his shoulder.

'Yes, but I mean like that, the way he did. . . .'

Clara looked at him, surprised. He looked away. 'Someday I'll tell you about it.' She did not press him. History, here in this country, did not interest her – especially anything to do with the last war. All that was something superimposed upon the essential reality of the land; it was part of the external order in which Clara and her colleagues were trapped. Underneath, everything conspired, secretly, invincibly, against history. On the esplanade, a perpetual flame, like those which burn before mausoleums and other monuments in the West to inspire the visitor's remembrance, reverence, or some like sentiment, flickered near the ground in the stifling air. It burned in a large aluminium tube, with too much fuel, too yellow a light, and trails of black smoke like the towers which burn off gas in oilfields. Civilization, victorious in death and war, was rather well served in this absurd memorial, exuding both the stench of industry and the glow of cremation.

Clara did not attempt to draw John away from his thoughts. She was used to his long spells of silence. He had started swimming again, at night in the pool. He was a perfectionist about diving and dreaded making a spectacle of himself. Clara, sitting on the opposite side from the diving board, could hardly see him. The nights were still very black at this time of year. Sometimes a long silence would follow the sound of the water closing over his body. No doubt John let the momentum carry him, or swam far below the surface.

Clara would call to him. He would answer. Then, hearing his calm voice through the shadow which filled the hollow of the pool, this voice to which the water gave a strange but reassuring resonance, as though someone had called to you from beneath some distant dome and had come to lead you with him into his vast, cool refuge of echoes and tranquillity, Clara knew that she had made the right choice, that with this man she would penetrate the darkness of truth, of joy, and turn her back, perhaps for ever, on the daylight of lies.

After a few days she agreed to join John in the pool. They

would swim about, losing and then finding one another, reaching out with wet hands to touch the other's laughing face. That evening, on the tiles next to the pool, they became lovers.

Meanwhile the holidays had come to an end, and those of the little group who had been vacationing by a lake, in the water of a once active volcano, the only slightly breezy place on the whole island, had come back to their duties in town. They had not mellowed. A series of little disasters had clouded their holiday. The Frenchwoman from UNESCO had broken her leg on a dangerous path, the wife of the British psychiatrist had fallen ill, and the Bolivian, upon his return, had discovered that his mule had died. Not even of malaria, either, but simply from exacerbation, disgust.

Clara learned all this from the Bolivian whose office was next to hers. He spoke in a dry tone of voice, as though she had been personally responsible for these unfortunate incidents. She understood; in the eyes of the others, she had sinned against the solidarity of the group, had treated herself to a good time with her scrap metal dealer, as they probably put it, while disaster struck the rest of them, But they were strong enough to overcome hardship, and magnanimous enough to want to help those who were in worse straits than themselves. Clara, in particular.

Softening his harsh tone, the Bolivian pointed out to her that she was making a great mistake. They had heard the worst possible reports about this John V. He did nothing, spent his time loitering about the city or gathering information about the wreckage left over from the last war.

'And then, you know, he's not the one with the fortune, it's his wife. We made inquiries at the embassy,' said the Bolivian in conclusion, lowering his voice, with a knowing look in his eye. Clara replied that she knew this. 'Well, in that case . . .' The man made a gesture of helplessness. None of this was of the slightest interest to him. I'm just telling it to you for what it's worth. . . .' The telephone rang. They could not replace his mule. Mules were rare in this region. But if he could use a horse, a small horse, naturally . . .' 'A small horse, you say. . . .' The Bolivian hesitated a moment. His glance met Clara's and darkened, grew serious, almost melancholy. 'Very well, I'll take it.'

Of course all this was rather cruel; the cage, the hobbled legs, the endless biting of the mosquitoes. . . . The Bolivian spent hours next to the animal, wearing gloves and netting over his face. He would even have stepped naked into the cage himself, if necessary. No price is too great when given the possibility of saving thousands, even millions of men, millions of children, you understand. No price was too great. He was sincere. His record of medical service revealed many dangerous missions, wounds received, diseases contracted. All the others in the group were capable of risking a life and limb for the cause, and some had proved it.

'No one has a right to be on the side of death.'

This was, in fact, the only observation made by the Bolivian, after having hung up the telephone. He could read Clara's thoughts. He knew that she was in the process of escaping the cage, breaking her ties, disrupting everything in her path, fleeing into the night. But the night is full of pitfalls, traps, lurking creatures, all the risks of relaxing one's vigilance. On the one hand a useful, anticipated, well-regulated death. On the other, far off in the darkness, a sacrifice of oneself, disorderly, futile. There was nothing in the world more unpardonable than being the victim of a single . . . But Clara did not intend to be anyone's prey. Her own, perhaps. What right had he to prevent her?

In the days that followed, the censure which her liaison with John had aroused from the start took on a different tone. It no longer seemed to be based on the fact that she had 'jilted' the others, so to speak. Nor did jealousy, or the regret, hidden under hypocritical moral principles, of never having had the courage to abandon themselves to passion, seem to lie behind their feelings. Politics had somehow become involved.

John's personality, which had been tolerated, with no questions asked, as long as he appeared to be just a passing acquaintance, was subject to the most rigorous scrutiny now that he asserted himself by staying in their midst and seducing Clara. Idle, or occupied with rather suspect projects, he was not identified with any of the forces which struggled, in one way or another, with economic underdevelopment.

One could perfectly well oppose the state of dependency in which the United States kept the people, in order to be allowed to transform each island into a military base; one could oppose the conniving attitude of the Philippine government, or, on the contrary, its undercurrents of neutralism; one could, with equal justification, oppose the underground activities of Marxist groups, or even the politically soporific work of international organizations. But it was utterly inconceivable that anyone should, through indifference, romantic self-indulgence, or a vague hope of profit, ally himself with the past, and revive the free-and-easy colonial spirit.

This new aspect of the conflict between her and the others in the group was all the more obvious to Clara in that, a month before, she herself might have passed similar judgement on John V. She discovered that until now she had belonged on the side of order, not only the order of the Occident, both scientific and Christian, but also a private order, in the religious sense, the kind which leads one to make sacrifices every day to an ideal of human progress, beyond parties or factions, in that precarious state of grace made possible by an international awareness.

She was reminded of this in no uncertain terms. The director of services in Southeast Asia, a former professor of the medical school in Peking, now in Formosa, summoned Clara to his office. A new 'operation' (the official term) in maternal and child health had been planned for Mindanao. Clara was asked to be the director. She requested two days to think it over and did not protest against this barely disguised excuse to banish her.

7*

She could not help but be impressed by the unanimity of the voices raised against her. The widely divergent origins of the members of the organization gave an extraordinary authority to their opinions. The fact that an Englishman, a Bolivian, an Israeli, a Frenchman, two or three Americans, still others, and above all, a Chinaman, joined together in condemning, or at least deploring, Clara's conduct could easily have led the young woman to question the validity of her own feelings.

It was too much of a simplification to say that all these people had become so denationalized within this organization and its administrative branches, that they now represented a single point of view in regard to morality. The Chinaman, after all, acted like a Chinaman, smiling, expressing himself in perfect English but with a kind of contempt for the language, as he told Clara of her appointment as head of the 'Mindanao operation'. How could this man, who preserved his native superstitions, who lived in the Chinese style at home, and worshipped his ancestors, how could he, in a private affair, to all appearances an 'affair of the heart', artificially adopt the point of view of Mlle Timonnier of UNESCO, born in Angoulême, or of Max Herrenschmidt who had come into the world on the shores of Lake Balaton?

No. There was only one answer: the whole world, from Buddhism to Judaism, from the Atlantic to Asia, was against Clara. And after all shouldn't this be a source of pride to her? By her attitude she was denouncing centuries of error, of contempt for freedom. Of course, had she been sure that she loved John, her convictions would have been stronger, and everything would have been simpler. In the union between them, and at the moment when it became a reality, Clara had found a slightly sad, gentle quality in John for which the men she had known had not prepared her. To be sure, there were moments even for the humblest of men when humility becomes a powerful asset. But because of the internal contradictions which are almost always present in the realm of sex, Clara was sometimes led to interpret her lover's lack of any desire to dominate as evidence of lukewarm emotions. And, in fact, one could hardly speak of passion in describing the relationship between Clara and John. It was fed by a mutual awareness of being excluded, of being strangers in the midst of society, and each was asking the other, in secret, for what was denied him in his incurable loneliness.

This world of theirs, beyond loneliness, had no name. Far out together, in a white hot furnace of light, a blank, silvery glare reflected from the still waters, exposing both heart and mind in raw nakedness, they still felt nostalgia, but not for anything terrestrial; their longing spun like the needle of a compass gone wild. Of course they could always lean over the cliff in the port and call out to America, Europe, or some other land, just for the sake of simplicity, because everyone needs something to cry out for, within himself; or they could bring their bodies close and pretend to seek the frantic, secondary communion of love; but all that was only a pretence, for lack of something better. The real longing, crying out from within, was nostalgia for oneself. But, for that, there are no words. Or perhaps, yes, there is one, a vague, very ambiguous word: 'freedom'.

And so, it was in the name of freedom that Clara decided not to go to Mindanao. John encouraged her. They would go to Leyte for a holiday. Clara asked for a two months' leave of absence, which was granted – the authorities expected as much. She and John settled not far from Tacloban, in one of those villages with a Mexican look which cluster about an enormous church, dating from the days of the conquistadors and full of black spiders. John had chosen this place because he had been there during the war, because the submerged stockpiles of military supplies were numerous, and some, he thought, still unknown, plentiful, and finally, because it was far away.

The feeling of isolation was not due entirely to the distance between this island and Manila, but also to the fact that it lay outside the main route of communication, and to the sparseness of the population. It somehow gave the impression of being, as they say, 'at the end of the world', not so much because of the long, deserted beaches violently outlined against a high black mass of vegetation, as because of certain almost deserted villages, where a man trudged slowly through the dust, with a hopeless look, like the last survivor of a team of explorers who had ventured rashly into the unknown.

The hotel where Clara and John stayed had only a few rooms with grilled doors made private by a curtain. The heat was intense. Clara and John spent hours on end lying naked on the rickety bed, staring at the brown cotton draped over the door. Now and then it stirred slightly, in a bit of breeze. Ever so slightly. It soon fell back into its original folds, rigid, as though lead weights had been sewed into the hem. The thin bamboo shades were just as motionless, also seemingly weighted with lead. Behind them was the sky, cloudless, of no particular colour, stretched across the horizon, always the same.

Although such immobility, such silence, made her feel a bit bored, Clara enjoyed a sense of complete detachment, during these periods of rest which had no fixed length. John seemed less relaxed. Since their arrival on the island, he had been driven by a sensual passion only half shared by Clara, but which never however seemed to her importunate or demanding. There was often, in John, a feminine gentleness, or more precisely, something which resembled the patient determination of a child. Little by little, through her companion's discretion, his long and frequent silences, Clara felt a world coming to the surface, a world of unspoken regrets, of stifled dreams, a trembling past which was indeed an expression of childhood and which she could also have found deep within herself. What if the need for freedom, for purity which possessed her were, in fact, only . . . But why reason so much? Freedom was there at hand.

Wrenching themselves from their lethargy, John and Clara would take walks, in the warm, dark shadows of the trees, along the rivers. John would often stop and look around, like someone who is trying to recognize where he is: war memories, no doubt. Clara felt slightly annoyed to see her companion turning their stroll, their discovery of an apparently virgin world, into a veteran's pilgrimage. John, of course, was supposed to be locating the military stockpiles that lay under water, but Clara grew more and more doubtful about the reality of this enterprise. Why would a man who had married into a family of rich, well-established industrialists bother with undertakings of this sort?

Nevertheless, he went with Clara to call upon an American in a nearby village whose address had been given him, and who might be able to provide some information. The man, a former GI who had stayed behind and married the daughter of a local Filipino official, owned a café and the only movie theatre in the village. Clara and John found him sitting at a table, drinking beer. He offered them some, and immediately explained that if one put a pinch of salt in the glass this mediocre brew was not unpleasant. Clara and John went along with the custom. An hour later, a dozen bottles of beer had been emptied; it went down like so much sea water.

The former GI was still young, a massive, red-headed man. His gaze was insensitive and his accent vulgar. Why had he remained behind? He explained that back in the United States he had worked as a refrigerator technician. He punched a time clock four times a day: slavery. Here he was able to forget the time, the day of the week, the date. He was warm. He had nothing to do, and sometimes lay in bed, reading, two days in a row. He had read all the books in English on the island, and in Manila where he sent for them. Beer, books: two kinds of thirst which he would never be able to quench. When he ran out of books and newspapers, he would sometimes have to read the labels on beer bottles over and over again. Happy? He looked at Clara as though he were going to hit her. Yes, completely happy. He would never go back to the United States. Did she understand? Never! A rather long silence followed this furious pronouncement.

Without revealing his plans to salvage the material, John led the ex-GI to talk about the military operations which had taken place on the island near the end of the war. John had participated but was not able to recognize where he had been. After landing, the troops had advanced blindly in the darkness, and during the day there had been several moments of great confusion and falling back. He had been disoriented. The ex-GI shook his head in a vague way. He didn't know anything about it. He had remained with the reserve troops on the ship until the end. Besides, why try to bring it all back again? He summed up the events which John had been describing in one filthy word. The two men looked at one another but soon lowered their eyes and looked away, ill-at-ease. Clara had a feeling that the man was a deserter.

She tugged discreetly at John's sleeve, to let him know she wanted to go. She was tired of sitting at this table laden with beer bottles and, for the last few minutes, she had even had the feeling of being contaminated. Seen through the conversation of the ex-GI, as the truth of his story came to light, the island began to seem like those barren outskirts of cities, which are full of outcasts, fugitives from justice, a whole population waiting about in idle vigilance and knowing no justice other than that of violence and vacant lots.

Clara, looking out the window in front of her, saw part of the village square, lonely, spread out, burned over. In the thin band of shade which ran along next to the row of hovels, separated one from the other by ditches of foul water, two grey pigs were snuffling about for garbage. Seen just then, in an instant of strictly photographic reality, prevented from explaining or justifying her situation, merely silhouetted in the bar against the depressing village scene, Clara might have seemed like a living example of tropical dereliction: ' . . . She washed up on Leyte . . .' She could hear the others in Manila saying this as clearly as if they had been in the room with her. 'Washed up?' But no! All she had to do was rouse herself, tear John away from these tiresome memories, these dismal wartime secrets.

When they finally left the bar, however, it was to visit an

aged Filipino, who served in a rather vague capacity as local registrar and reporter, and who had kept a record of the military action on the island in 1944. The ex-GI had eventually suggested that John go to see him. After all, since it interested him so . . . The old man had observed the movement of each American combat unit; he was believed to have passed on this information to the Japanese.

The writer – for this was what he called himself – lived in a rather large, rickety, wooden house. Slats were missing from the walls and even from the floor. He was lying on a cot and rose in haste when the servant girl, in rags, let in Clara and John. His eyes looked distracted. He moved about in fits and starts: he had the most terrible headache! Walking across the room in bare feet, at an odd, somehow disconcerting pace, he stopped abruptly, and turned about, his hand on his brow. Why had they come? He asked John to repeat what he had just said. 'Oh, yes. Very well. I am going to write it down for you. I will draw a map. What time is it please? I will write it for you; I will write it down for you. I will need paper and ink. . . .' Sentences out of a foreign language phrasebook, enunciated with painful deliberation.

The man seemed to be really suffering. When Clara had questioned him, as a doctor, earlier, he had replied, 'I think it is the island fever or else, or else . . .' He had not finished his sentence. A nervous mannerism. He couldn't seem to find the words. Clara had looked up at the ceiling and his eyes had followed hers: a great many spider webs, too many not to have been deliberately preserved by the master of the house. They were a natural protection against the evil spells of the 'aswangs', and at the same time proved to visitors that the host himself was not an aswang, a demonic creature who was transformed into an animal every night. But did the old writer really escape this metamorphosis? His severe migraine, his random gestures, were like symptoms of a guilty conscience, of nocturnal wanderings, the immense fatigue that follows transmutation and a return to the original state. . . . The spider webs were only an ineffective filter, a flimsy veil. 'This island is not good,' said the old man. 'This island is not good,' Clara repeated to herself. She felt happy; her love of darkness was being fulfilled.

Still holding his forehead, the old man finally seated himself at a table and drew a piece of yellow paper before him. He dipped a cheap schoolboy's pen several times into an encrusted inkwell. 'The 25th Division. . . . No, the 24th Division . . .'

'Five dollars, please,' said the old man, without raising his head.

John took the money from his pocket and put it on the table. With a trembling hand, the old man began to draw winding lines and arrows, and to fill in names and numbers. John was leaning over his shoulder and following his work with something more than attentive interest, almost with anxiety. But that was the river they had walked along this morning! Not far enough, apparently. Slightly further, it joined another tributary, and just beyond was the sector of the 25th division. . . . No, the 24th, I beg your pardon, this splitting headache. . . .'

Clara had stopped being impatient. The severe tension which had begun to appear on John's face a few moments earlier made her think that he was not simply trying to revive military memories, with the nostalgic pride characteristic of veterans, but instead, to rediscover a place where memory had been abruptly cut off, a break in his past. She had to help him, if she could. She began to discover that not only did freedom lie outside history and the order it has gradually imposed, but it is also buried in that part of ourselves which our own history had blotted out. So many steps to retrace. Salvation lay upstream.

'Upstream, a little further upstream . . .' Clara marvelled at how, for some time now, the water had become an everpresent symbol. The water was a language of its own, rich with meaning, which she could hear, could understand, a little more clearly every day. Thrust by chance into this semi-aquatic country, she had found the key, the essential key which she had sought for so long. 'Still a little further upstream . . .' Clara and John, stumbling now and then, were making their way through the dense vegetation, following the river which the old writer had marked on his map.

They had passed the place where the tributaries met. John gave a sudden shout and stopped. The reflection of the sun on the moving water danced on his face and mirrored the excitement within his mind. It was here. All at once, everything came back. John sat on the river bank, talking, now and then throwing handfuls of dirt into the river. It was here . . .

He had reached this bank, out of breath, deafened, blinded with fear. The enemy, after a staccato burst of machine-gun fire, beneath the whine of shells, like the sound of guitar strings breaking, had suddenly emerged from the jungle, a swarm of little men, almost the same colour as the leaves, bent double, running as though they were holding a package clasped to their chests. They descended upon you, their heads wobbling beneath their helmets, as though participating in one of those grotesque children's races, in which the runners are handicapped by an egg on a spoon, by a sack around their feet, or here, the mysterious burden that made them bend over double; a rifle, a box of machine-gun shells, a flame thrower. . . . What could you do?

In a few seconds there would be a row of chests breaking through the thin white ribbon of the finish line, a stampede, a sudden flash, and then the final darkness. John had had the absurd, fleeting impression of being the target for all these wobbling heads. He felt as though he were within a huge smashed guitar – the Philippines, painted with childish scenes, too blue, too green, in the cheap Hawaiian taste cultivated by the native boys, in decorating their rooms, their motorcycles, in their choice of postcards, their sportshirts, the songs they sang to please the girls or to express their desire, their desire that was so crude, so canine, essentially so sad, easily brought down to earth by a slap, the kind of sudden, cold slap that takes one back all at once to certain grey evenings in autumn, to the sorrows and the humiliations of childhood. . . .

And as the Japanese were running towards him (their little legs, in puttees, were as thick at the ankle as at the calf) John had felt the same kind of slap coming, but unbearable this time, too violent, too 'dirty', with the blood you taste on your lip when a friend knocks you down, and a strange smell of fire and sulphur, as though someone in a dream, as though someone were burning something you couldn't see, because you were going to die. . . . Then John had fled, all this was too unfair, too stupid. . . .

The vines tangled around his feet. It had not been easy to flee, one had to persevere. He had penetrated a kind of thicket and had found himself on the bank of the river. On the opposite side, three Japanese, lying behind the bushes, were taking aim at him. He could see their faces, almost without eyes, as if swollen by the sun. He had thrown up his arms and dropped his gun in the river. Just at that moment a volley of shells had burst, like a geyser spurting right behind him. He had plastered himself to the ground. There were a half-dozen more explosions and then silence. Without getting up, John had looked across the river. The three Japanese had disappeared. . . . There it was: a coward. . . .

Clara shrugged her shoulders. None of this mattered in the least. John agreed with her right away, as though all he had needed were this absolution. No, it did not matter in the least, but the memory had been bothering him for a long time. Only now could he see it in perspective. The reality of the place where it had happened, the bank, the narrow river, the trees, the plants, the colour of the ground, put the experience back into its natural setting, did away with the allegorical reverberations in his memory, and very nearly reduced the incident to a curious little adventure, one of the unexpected hazards of a vacation in the tropics.

'The gun must still be there. . . .'

John took off his clothes, stripping right down to his bathing suit. He smiled. He would have a look, just for the fun of it, the way one might enjoy putting back together the pieces of some ridiculous object found in an attic, an object which still evokes vague but somehow tender memories.

Though a bit anxious, for there was a note which did not ring true in John's sudden playfulness, Clara did not try to stop him. He had to go still further, still deeper. This story about losing his nerve, running away, was superficial. The beginning of it all lay back before the gun, the war . . . John's head came out of the water again. He hadn't seen anything. Was this really the place where he had thrown it, after all? For miles along, the river bank looked very much the same.

They kept walking along the river. The heat was intense, the sun white-hot. If only sweat were black, could protect one entirely. It was no protection, only a wet but scalding cape over one's shoulders. At every step, John thought he recognized the exact spot where he had arrived that day, breathless, stumbling against one last root and almost falling, probably ridiculous in the eyes of the three Japanese who lay there, motionless, with the alert somnolence of fishermen watching their lines. . . . John dove, found nothing at the bottom, came back to the surface laughing and shouting at Clara to join him: the water was extraordinarily cool. Clara hesitated. She did not make up her mind until somewhat later, when John discovered a large heap of military supplies under the water.

It had belonged to the Japanese – John could tell from the writing on a mud-covered box of ammunition which he brought to the surface – and was spread out over a rather large area, five or six metres deep. In spite of the way it was heaped together, and the murkiness of the water, he could make out not only large quantities of ammunition, but also several small artillery pieces, miscellaneous other weapons, radio equipment and a few small vehicles: enough to bring in a good sum, considering the local price of metal and explosives in the country. John hesitated about undertaking this salvage work, which was very risky, and promised only uneven profits. However, he had to find some means of earning a living.

Clara was surprised. He had never mentioned his financial

situation and she had believed it was well-assured. Yes, but what if he got a divorce? . . . They had returned to their hotel room and were lying there, stretched out. The brown curtain hanging over the grillwork door stirred slightly now and then, but not because of a breeze. It was only the air displaced by a barefoot serving boy, passing along the corridor. Clara discovered a dead insect stuck to her thigh, It was flat and grey, with long feelers on either side, fins or antennae. It had probably settled on her in the water. . . . Not long before, opening her eyes in the light-flecked depths of the river, she had seen a thousand little bodies moving in a slow whirlpool, with sidereal regularity, trapped in eternal rotation, whether living or dead she could not tell, for death did not add to their weight, or deliver them from the cycle. And so it was, perhaps, as far back as memory could reach. . . . No doubt everything began long ago for John, before this gun in the river, but everything also began 'afterwards'. A circle – everything beginning everywhere.

John's company had been moved after the attack, and had caught up with him by the river bank. He had been turned over to the military police and put in prison. One of his uncles, a colonel, had intervened and spoken to the psychiatrist assigned to prisoners coming up for court martial. Nervous breakdown, a history of previous mental disorders, cranial injury on the football field in college, an emotionally deprived childhood (adulterous mother deserting the home). . . . In short, a year of prison, victory, and the clemency which comes with peace. . . .

With the tips of her fingernails, Clara had been able to pluck the dead insect from her thigh. A little pink mark was left, just where it had been. There were other stories—also without end – within the venom. To circle about in the water, outside of time, was not so important. Within these organisms, often microscopic, another kind of motion was going on, swift, directional (she imagined so many little arrows, as in the swarming of bees) revealing a power (which might as well be a magic one, for how could one be sure about anything so far removed from the senses?) the power of the toxins active in the venom, moving like particles of gold and iron, especially of gold. . . .

'. . . And in spite of this he goes on talking, apparently to the brown curtain over the door, the curtain that answers by moving slightly when anyone goes by, barefoot, in the corridor. He says that he married without love, because his wife was rich and because he was a coward. He breathes deeply and one can see – the paunchiness of the forties barely showing on him – the scalloped edges of his ribs, just before the concavity of his belly: a worn-out swimmer. . . . Cowardice is a bottomless ocean. Once on the banks, those who are saved gasp deeply for breath. One knows that they will eventually grow fat. But what truth is glimpsed by cowards! They are saved; they seem to be saved; but they have known something deep, total, and dazzling, like drowning. . . .'

The next day they went back to the river. John wanted to draw up an inventory of the sunken supplies. In reality – and Clara was not taken in – this was only a pretext. John was not going to get a divorce, and therefore would have no need to earn his living in this country which he would soon leave. Clara, after all, did not expect her companion to cut off all ties so that they could be joined together, legally or not. She had been drawn to him simply because he seemed engaged in a quest, the goal of which she felt must be freedom. She had forgotten one thing, however, that freedom bears our own name, our own face and that all our attempts to escape the world that oppresses us bring us back to ourselves, to the scrutiny of our own past. How many of the long-gone events which hold us trapped are we able to subdue, much less erase?

It was obvious that John, in returning to the river, was trying to prove to himself that his desertion during the war had not been anything serious, had been a fairly common reaction: all these Japanese who had got rid of their weapons here! Each time he dove he found more, some overgrown with aquatic

plants or buried beneath part of the bank which had caved in,
others half-upright and camouflaged by roots: a deserted battle-
field trembling in the powdery translucence of the water, a
broad, devastated encampment in which only the algae moved
about, undulating slowly. How distant it all seemed from flags
and victory! This watery silence, where weapons lay submerged, jettisoned, abandoned to a kind of vegetable metamorphosis, affirmed man's wisdom, his love of peace, of life,
his contempt for the clichés of heroism and his desire for freedom in spite of everything. . . .

Yes, in spite of everything. . . . When John came back up to
the surface he spat: the taste of mud. . . . Once again a staleness
became noticeable in the water, just as it had the evening when
John had come out of the pool, and met Clara for the first time.
Now she was sitting on the bank. He could not see her very
well for her face was in shadow. Besides, John was a bit dazed
by the reflections of the sun on the water. He had a slight headache. The island was not good, as the old writer had said.

Three young Filipinos, emerging from the trees, came up
behind Clara. She turned around and saw them. They greeted
her. She answered, and then, since she was in a bathing suit
and the presence of the three men, so close by, made her uncomfortable, she dove into the water. She swam over to John,
but before she reached him, she went under again, towards the
river bed. John did the same. He caught a glimpse of her,
through the water, her body arched, sweeping the water away
in front of her with broad strokes, not turning her head towards
him, unable to hear or see him, already moving away and
starting to curve upwards towards the surface.

When he found her again, she was doing a dead man's float,
her eyes closed, as indifferent, as aloof as she had been in the
depths. He was about to talk to her when the sound of three
bodies, plunging into the water one after the other, made him
turn back towards the bank. The three Filipinos were swimming towards them. Clara had righted herself and was treading
water, like a water-polo player. She looked at the Filipino who

was nearest her, smiled, and said a few words, the kind people exchange while swimming: 'Feels good, doesn't it?'

The man was very handsome, with teeth that gleamed when he laughed. He was about to answer, when Clara, with a suddenness which, to John, seemed provocative, turned and dove straight to the bottom. The Filipino followed her. John let himself sink, but he was too far behind to see them, and, worn out from all his diving, his headache growing more and more painful, he had to come up quickly for air.

Clara, too, had swum back to the surface. The Filipino lingered under water. He came up right next to Clara, said something to her which John did not understand, and then spoke in Tagalog to his two friends who were swimming slightly further away. He probably said something to them about the submerged weapons, for they immediately dove under. Clara, once again, floated motionless on the surface. The Filipino looked at her. He dove beneath her, playfully. Clara swam away at a rapid crawl.

The two boys had come back up, carrying a box of ammunition which they left on the bank. Clara dove under again. She could feel the Filipino swimming very close to her. His hand grazed her thigh. It was probably not deliberate, for he was already moving away, at an angle, long, lithe, blowing silvery bubbles from his mouth. Clara tried to follow him but she was out of breath. . . . She had been at the top for several seconds when the Filipino rose from the water next to her, pushing his hair back with one hand.

'How can you stay under so long?'

He leapt slightly out of the water, showing his brown, muscular torso which he slapped with the palm of his hand, and laughed, before letting himself fall back, his arms outstretched, with a great splash. His two friends had salvaged another box of ammunition and were laying it on the bank. The man shouted to them in Tagalog. Clara could catch only one word: 'night'. They waved, in agreement, and suddenly at a loose end, sat down on the ground and began to scratch their toes. Clara looked around; John was no longer in the water. She saw him on the bank opposite the two Filipino boys. The man was their leader, probably . . .

'Look: like this . . . almost empty,' he said to Clara.

He stopped smiling, tipped back slowly, exhaling, his chest contracting, his muscles standing out, and sank into the water which closed over him: blissful, dead, already invisible. . . . Clara, too, closed her eyes, emptied her lungs, and tipped backwards: night, the cool water over her face. . . . But all at once, in the sudden joy of mobility within a new element, she opened her eyes again and swam very fast towards the murky depths, towards this creature who did not seem a part of anything she had ever known, except her childhood dreams, legends, the great, inaccessible myths of pleasure and happiness. . . .

. . . She did not see him coming; he was rising from the depths to meet her, slowly, his legs folded beneath him, his hands extended, reaching out, his eyes half closed. He seized her by the waist and she felt the cool pressure of his palms, even cooler than the water. She tried to swim to the surface. He held her back. To pull away, she had to press on the man's head for a moment, tangling her fingers in his hair. Then he rose to her level, grabbed her hands – she was not afraid – and let himself float to the surface with her. The daylight broke over them.

Dazzled, gasping for breath, Clara did not swim away. The man was talking to her. She could not answer. Her hair streaming over her face; she must have been a fright. . . . What was he saying? At night the water was even cooler. If she could come, that evening, to the same place, right after sunset. . . . She smiled and swam away, watching her form, towards the bank where John was waiting.

His face was rather drawn. Jealousy, or migraine? Jealousy, more likely, but the jealousy of bitter resignation. He admitted it. Seated on the river bank, while Clara was playing in the water with the Filipino, he had felt, in spite of his resentment, and almost with relief, that he was getting what he deserved, not from her, for she was acting without conscious intent, but from some superior power which he did not name; in short, he was discovering the logic of fate.

Now, almost at the spot where he had shown cowardice a few years before, he found his punishment: the sight of his mistress caressed by another man, under the water. Or rather, he inflicted this punishment on himself, by not having the courage to chase away the Filipino or take Clara home; but if he did so, if he sat there without moving, it was because he felt that these things were willed 'from above', and that the only way he could redeem himself was to reach that state of extreme humility which lies underneath cowardice.

He had to resign himself: for him there would never be anything but loneliness, the loneliness which had begun in childhood and to which, every time he found himself in society, among his equals, almost accepted by them, he would invariably return, choosing the paths of cowardice and fear. Fear, he found everywhere. He had come to this country to get away from a woman he did not like, who got on his nerves, and also to try to exorcize at least one part of his past – the war memories – but, almost immediately, the country began to frighten him. He felt trapped, as though there might be no more ships, as though the planes might all be grounded and he might be cut off forever from that part of the world where daily humiliation, contempt for oneself, had at least the allure of slothfulness and familiarity. It was fear, also, that drew him towards Clara and fear that was making him lose her.

After having listened to him, she shrugged her shoulders; she might as well appear to dismiss these thoughts as idle fancies, even though she saw the truth in them all too clearly. It was true that John was losing her, and she had been aware of this for the last few days. She had run headlong into the man's past, his withdrawn, fearful, childhood-ridden past, his indestructible past which blocked their way towards the sources of freedom. But how far could she herself go? The joy she had felt a few minutes before, in the river, remained a mystery to her; was it merely sensual pleasure? Why had it seemed so complete, so fulfilling, and been accompanied by such feelings of contentment, even more than that, of truth?

As she walked back to the village, with John, who was now silent, she was thinking about how to return to the river that evening. She would never dare to go alone. Anyway, would John let her? Cowards can become stubborn, all of a sudden. Besides, he had told her too much; now he had to contradict himself. Clara told him that when the three Filipinos spoke to one another in dialect, she had caught a few words, and that she thought they were planning to go back at night to collect some of the munitions. John didn't believe this; they would have needed equipment, underwater searchlights. It was curiosity over this one detail, quite unnecessary, since he had given up his own plans to salvage the material, that made him decide to go back that night with Clara.

There were other motives, too: a sacrifice to absurdity; a desire to undertake this rather long, perilous excursion in the darkness, through the creeping vines, the insects; a desire to go to the limit of revolt and suffering (the three Filipinos could overpower him and rape Clara) – all this hidden, veiled by his apparent interest in whether the three men had searchlights, and by his eagerness to see the strange vestiges of war brought slowly to the surface, streaming with algae, the black, cleansed weapons which could never stop coming to the surface of his memory, waterlogged guns, now rough as bark, cannons from a shipwrecked galley, corroded handgrenades like heavy, over-sized sea-shells, a dead soldier's helmet with bullet holes on the side (or in the back, the soldier having been shot down as he fled) through which a stream of water first gushed, then trickled, and finally dried up, as it was laid on the river bank ... and, at the bottom of all this, the desire to disappear, for sooner or later one tries to elude one's fear, like an unwanted household animal, and, even more deeply hidden, invisible, the wish that Clara, too, should disappear.

When they reached the spot, it was not yet dark. The three Filipinos were there, next to an old jeep which they had driven through the jungle. The man who had swum with Clara that morning barely looked at her. He strolled brazenly up to John, and began to speak to him, in bad English, with a kind of aggressive familiarity. He had been told that John was exploring the river, in order to write a history book. The way the Filipino said this, it sounded like 'story' book, and he dwelt on the word at length, as though it were even stranger to him than the others. Had John, while looking for the 'story' of the river, found any other heaps of weapons and ammunition under the water? John shook his head, 'No.' Then he laughed, all of a sudden, in a voice Clara had never heard, shrill, forced, grotesque: there was probably a gun, somewhere, a little further on. . . . The Filipino did not seem to understand.

'Did the old writer tell you what I was doing?' asked John.

The man did not answer. He was in a bathing suit, but had kept on his light shirt. Slipping his hands beneath his trunks, he stroked his groin and then turned, preoccupied, towards the jeep. The darkness deepened. The two other Filipinos slipped into the water. Each had a flashlight, bound with waterproof tape, fastened to the belt of his brief, dirt-streaked bathing suit. Clara sat down at the foot of a tree, while John went close to the water, a bit further upstream, to watch the boys who had started to dive, after swimming out to the middle of the river.

Clara knew that the man would come over to her. Not right away. He was diving now, too, and Clara, with her eyes closed, could hear the sound of the three men swimming – the same sound, but louder, more confused, which she had heard in the swimming pool outside the dining room of the club. That solitary splashing which had obsessed her for so long, how ridiculous it seemed, all of a sudden! The darkness which covered everything was extraordinarily silent in the moments when the water, stretching out further than the eye could see, was not being slapped, shaken, swept aside; the three men were literally forcing open the river. . . . The man would come.

No doubt he just wanted to get the two boys started in their work. . . .

Clara grew aware of the power of those denials which had sustained her so consistently over the years. How absurd her pride had been! Her too-thoroughly feminine vocation, her calling to 'MCH' which was at once her definition and the thorn in her side, could in fact become her way towards truth and freedom. Perhaps not always – but at any rate, here, to-night – in this primeval darkness, where, beneath the weight of the man who was coming at any minute now, she could at last luxuriate in her own passivity, in her own servility.

He was coming. She heard the grass rustling beneath his feet. It was now completely dark. Clara must have dozed. He was looking for her, could not see her. 'Who is it?' He came up to her, whispering something or other, 'Are they asleep?' and crouched, reached out his hand. . . . All of a sudden everything was denied, annihilated, things known, things read and heard, thoughts about oneself and others, the idea of freedom, of truth; the whole firm, smooth surface of the world, pulverized. . . . An explosion shook the air. Clara saw flames. Were they then so close? The Filipino leapt to his feet. She ran behind him. Was it John, perhaps?

No. He was there, standing on the bank, a bit haggard. A grenade, more likely a mine, had exploded in the hands of one of the two divers. Torn to shreds, probably. Why look for his body? There was no body: only a drop of shark's blood, added to the nocturnal waters. . . .

'Oh, to die, now, this very second!' thought Clara, with all her might, her eyes closed. But it is always the others who die, just as our happiness becomes most piercing. How many eyes close forever, next to us, in bewilderment, suffering, or hardship, in silence and solitude, while we, who long for this crowning fulfilment, find only the deceptive veil of sleep, already torn, shot through with tomorrow's light. . . .

The next morning, some policemen came to the hotel and took John and Clara to Tacloban, to question them. Alerted by the explosion, a patrol had been sent out the night before and had stopped the jeep as it drove, loaded with explosives, through a village near the river. The two occupants of the vehicle had been sought by the police for a long time. They belonged to the Huk movement of radical guerrilla partisans organized at the end of the war. When peace was declared, their forces were dispersed by the government, and only a few small bands were left, living by robbery and assault.

The police were interested in finding out whether John, who had been noticed several times wandering along the river, was an accomplice of these men, had shown them the location of the munitions and helped in the salvage work. They had found out that he had made a thorough inquiry as to the probable position of these sunken arsenals. Clara never knew what he said to the police. She was questioned in another room. The fact that she belonged to an international organization gave her a sort of diplomatic immunity, and she was soon freed. A policeman was ready to take her to the airport, where, in an hour, an aeroplane was leaving for Manila. Her vacation was over, wasn't it? They needed to question John at length. He could join her back there.

She did not wait for him in Manila. She had decided to go back to the States as soon as possible. All of a sudden, she found the country suffocating. It offered nothing but the wild impulses of loneliness and if sometimes, like the night before, there was a bit of happiness to be enjoyed, it left the aftertaste of guilt, of cheating which follows dreams. Everything which Clara had experienced, in the last few months, was a result of being in a strange country, out of her element. The disadvantage of this condition is that it deprives one of the landscapes of resignation and contentment, those which allow one to live, more or less happily, with oneself. Without realizing it, she had been stricken by violent nostalgia, not the kind that throws one against the parapets of harbours, but the kind that makes one plunge in desperate confusion to the very depths of oneself.

Besides, Clara belonged to that race of human beings who

will never easily find peace of mind, wherever they are. For if you take away all the supports, the multiple truths, resting one on top of the other, overlapping, mingled, juxtaposed, our world is like an ice floe cracking as it thaws, a mountain of angles, and we must keep on running, buffeted endlessly from side to side, wounded, in the narrow confines of a triangle, amidst an infinite number of other triangles. . . .

translated by Merloyd Lawrence

The Women

No one ever knew how the first one had come. Hardly had it made its presence known, when it burst into a multitude, becoming one with its progeny, weaving its burning trail into the immense web which its species spreads over the misery of man, like an ancient, decomposing embroidery.

No, it was just as impossible to single out the first louse as the first flame in a roaring fire; everyone was already ignited. As for the origins of this adventurous parasite, whose identity would have to remain abstract, all one could say was that it bore witness to the existence of extremely subtle social contacts between people.

Few solitudes are exclusive enough to fool vermin. They alone can trace and confirm the most furtive of relationships; they alone dare to remind the most unsociable human beings of their dealings with others. They alone, as humble servants of a universal complicity, draw everyone into that woefully promiscuous world which germs and lice now and then disclose behind the deceptive façade of life.

It chose, or rather they chose, for lice, like hailstones, are always on the verge of plurality, old Bolinka, one of the oldest

of the Ukrainian women in the labour camp at Schweinemünde.

'I've had an itch,' she said sheepishly to the German who ran
the camp, one evening as she came back from the factory, 'for
at least two days now. . . .'

The Ukrainian interpreter who stood next to the desk kept
after her with questions: 'Had she come in contact with anyone
from outside the camp? Which other women in the camp had
lice?'

Actually, during the interrogation, the word was hardly ever
used. They said, 'I have them, you have them, they have them,
how could anyone have got them?' overcome by a modesty
which, nevertheless, did not reduce the possibility of violence.
These sibylline utterances, moreover, soon conjured up an
enormous grey shadow, bristling with antennae and angular
pincers, which floated high over the barracks, indeed over all
of Pomerania.

Sometimes a German would toss the word out as a kind of
coarse joke. Everyone would laugh, with horror like a stone
in his gullet; the louse caused the same reaction as a loose rat,
a scrambling for chairs and a shaking of skirts. But soon the
German tightened the noose, trapping the parasite beneath it's
contemptuous scrutiny: lice were generally found only on
members of inferior races, the Russians, in particular.

'Good God, haven't you ever heard of civilization?'

There it was: the mask of shame, the first creeping, itching
sensations. Asia swarms over us all.

The protests took on a childish note:

'But I swear to you, at home, before the war, only
beggars . . .''

'What about that sheep bone?' the German would ask
triumphantly. 'What did you use that sheep bone for?'

This was one of the most recent and precious of German
archaeological discoveries. In certain remote farms of the
Ukraine, soldiers of the invading army had found large, flat
bones which mothers ran through their children's hair to crush

vermin. How could the inmates of Schweinemünde fight back when such a weapon had fallen into enemy hands?

Old Bolinka stood with her head bowed, no doubt aware of the strict distance which her cross-examiners now maintained betwen themselves and her. The louse was in her left armpit, she could have sworn, but the two questioners no doubt expected to see her swarm with vermin then and there.

'Get away from here,' yelled the interpreter. 'Tomorrow you'll stay in camp. You'll boil all your clothes, everything, do you understand? Even your underwear. You'll wash, and shave every hair on your body. That will mean two days off, but don't let us catch you lousy after that!'

Bolinka crept quietly back to the dormitory, said nothing to anyone, and sat down on her bed, keeping her vermin to herself, her teeming secret.

'Do you know,' she finally said to her neighbour who was finishing her black bread, half stretched out on her cot, 'I'm not going to the factory tomorrow. Or the day after, either. . . .'

Her face was glowing with still-hesitant joy.

'Oh, really?' said the other woman, with her mouth full, forgetting to chew for a moment. 'Why?'

'I have lice,' murmured Bolinka, lowering her eyes. 'Well, what could I do about it? They came, just like that. Anyway, tomorrow I'm going to sleep until eight o'clock, yes, at least until eight, and then afterwards I'll kill them. . . .'

She went on talking about her lice, how many there were, their mysterious origins, but her neighbour was already broadcasting the news around the dormitory, The forty women, who were getting ready for bed, did not bother to show disgust; envy was stronger. Sleep was the one light of their existence. Being able to sleep until eight o'clock meant a morning of glory. Only after the others left for the factory, around six o'clock, did a second sleep carry you high on to a hilltop, in the brilliance of a summer dawn, or a sparkling Christmas frost, and leave you there, limp with laziness, to wallow in memory.

8

And the day which lay ahead would be free, disengaged from the lathe which rasped in a stench of hot metal, free of shrill commands and threats. The threats, these days, came from the sky. The roar of the lathes and rotary drills drowned out all other sounds and the sky did not sound out until the Allied planes were already overhead, with the whistle of bombs already in the wind. You died almost without having heard that you were dying.

The camp was far enough away from the factory to be out of danger, and besides, the sky could be seen there all day long: bright, clear, but above all, silent. Salvation lay in being able to hear the sky. Such was Bolinka's newfound happiness. It was well worth the rosary of smarting bites which she was counting with her fingertips in the darkness of the dormitory. Tireless vermin, sleepless desire, endless tears: all night long, Bolinka scratched like a dog behind a locked door. The pent-up lice kindled an impatience for morning.

Bolinka's glory ended in the laundry room, in a cloud of steam. Deloused, she went back to work in the factory. The days passed. Death migrated overhead, so imminent at times that when the planes flew very low with a thunderous roar, their shadows passed over the sunlit grass like running trout: this land was now the bed of a torrent.

One evening, as the women were returning to camp, breaking ranks and shouting impatiently at each other for no reason except to impress themselves, one of them went up to the interpreter. She stood on one leg and then the other, looking down at the ground while the interpreter grew restless waiting.

'That's right,' sighed the woman, 'I caught them. Maybe it was from Bolinka, the other day . . .'

'Bolinka!' cried the interpreter. 'But that was more than a month ago! They certainly took their time getting to you. . . .'

'But then . . .' asked the women, looking up. 'How . . . ?'

Obsequious, stupid, she was begging for an explanation. She did not deserve to be treated this way, to be left alone all of a sudden. She had just lost Bolinka, with whom, a moment earlier, she at least shared the comforting bond of resentment. There was no reason for this disgrace. Nothing had happened; she lived from day to day without thinking, and suddenly, the lice were all over her like ants on a tree, and she began to sense, in this atmosphere of fleeting shadows, black storm clouds disintegrating in the wind, swift whining shapes that darted over the earth, death running like trout, that her shame was part of an original sin which a mysterious God was spreading over the sunlit land.

But now – the thought came very suddenly – she should rejoice. The woman had not yet had time to realize that the lice would bring her two days of rest. Absolution so complete that it became suspect, leaving a sickly-sweet taste behind. Forgiveness could have been calmly accepted, but this dividend of grace almost erased the sin and went so far beyond mere rehabilitation that it was almost a reward, an honour.

The interpreter, meanwhile, led the woman into the camp director's office. He was a bitter old man, whom the hazards of war had made the guardian of a hoard of femininity, as though his superiors had recognized in him the asset of castration. Had age not already protected him from desire, this paradise for virility would have offered him only tasteless delights. Russians were so sexually degraded that only the chastening power of rape could transfigure them for a brief instant. But that was impossible without the excitement of battle, a warrior's anonymity.

The old man raised his head, exasperated: What did this one want?

The interpreter had seated herself a certain distance from the culprit.

'She has lice,' she said, with a wry face, trying to exaggerate her disgust. 'What shall I do, give her two days off, like the last one, to clean up?'

'Just a moment, please!' cried the camp director, raising his hand, which was thick-set, with blunt fingernails. 'In the first place, would you please tell me how she caught the lice? That's what I'd like to know!'

He swung his chair about so as to face the interpreter. She blinked, surprised by this sudden attack.

'I'm not any better informed than you,' she murmured. Hardly had she finished uttering these words when she felt an itch on her side, slightly below her armpit. She must not scratch, at any cost; it would be too humiliating. She knew she was safe from vermin, that this was merely the incendiary effect of the lice, whose name alone aroused suspicions and burning sensations. She bit her lip: another itch awoke somewhere on her belly.

'It happens to be your *job* to be better informed,' replied the camp director, dwelling on each syllable and staring at her. 'It is your *responsibility*, Mariouchka!'

Now it was excruciating. Perhaps if she did not answer, the director would finally look away, and she would then be able, with one discreet fingernail, to relieve the fire that was torturing her. So she simply hung her head, trying to look repentant. Eaten alive, she suddenly found herself in a state of guilt which she never could have anticipated a moment earlier. Then she couldn't bear it any longer. Attempting to cross her arms as a feeble disguise, she began to scratch herself furiously under her armpit.

'All this talk about lice . . .' she muttered, turning scarlet.

The director burst out laughing and turned to the culprit, the woman with the straggly hair who was still standing in front of his desk.

'What about you, aren't you scratching?' he asked.

When put in this way the question sounded absurd. It was like an impromptu invitation, as though the old German expected at any moment to be surrounded by simian frenzies. The woman, who understood some German, replied too quickly.

'No, I'm not scratching,' she said, shaking her yellow hair.

'Splendid!' exclaimed the German, hitting the table with the palm of his hand. 'Splendid! She's not scratching but the

interpreter is. Yes, you!' he snapped, pointing at the interpreter whose fingers were still clawing at the grey material of
her dress, somewhere near her pubis. 'Who knows, maybe
they caught them from you!'

The interpreter pulled herself together, rose, and wriggled
slightly to adjust her clothing. Her itching had stopped. She
gave the director an obsequious smile.

'What have you decided?' she asked with her usual seriousness, to show that the joke had ended. But she was not too
sure. No, she was not sure that it had been a joke at all, not sure
that this sudden, grotesque nightmare was over. The director
seemed to be savouring it. Once again he turned to the other
woman.

'This is a strange business,' he said, reverting to his former
severity. 'But I'm not as stupid as you might think. No, I'm
not so easily taken in. I would be only too delighted to give
you time to wash off your filth and vermin, you charming
creature, since the camp hygiene depends on it. But look here!
I want proof. Do you understand? Proof! It would be all too
easy to get off work this way. Now,' he concluded, sitting
back in his chair, 'show me your lice!'

The woman seemed disoriented and just stared at the interpreter.

'The director told you to show him your lice!' the interpreter
cried shrilly, exasperated by the whole affair.

'But I'm not sure where they are right now,' muttered the
woman. 'I would have to take all my clothes off and look for
them on my body or in the folds of the cloth. . . . Tell him that
it doesn't matter. I can get along with them; I'll go to the
factory tomorrow. . . .'

'What is she rattling on about!' yelled the old German, sitting up in his chair. 'Why all this discussion?'

'Tell him I withdraw my complaint,' cried the woman, suddenly afraid.

'She says she withdraws her complaint,' translated the
interpreter.

The statement was absurd. She wished she had thought before translating it, but it was all part of this lice business which they would never see the end of.

'Her complaint?' asked the director, flabbergasted. 'She says she withdraws her complaint! What complaint? And whom is she complaining about?'

The interpreter shrugged her shoulders. No, she really shouldn't have translated that absurd statement.

'Well?' shouted the old German, 'What are you waiting for? Ask her. Or are you trying to drive me out of my mind tonight?'

The interpreter was about to reply, to explain that it was only an unfortunate choice of words, but the director's angry glance left her tongue-tied.

'Against whom did you wish to lodge a complaint?' she finally asked the woman, whose only thought now was to get away from here, and who had already taken a step, sideways, towards the door, without attracting the attention of the others.

When she heard the interpreter's question, the woman blushed with embarrassment; her hair seemed even yellower. It was so like her! Here she was, already at fault, and just at the moment when she was about to reap a fantastic reward from her humiliation, her lice, her wretched carelessness, she had to start blaming others!

It was true, she had said something about a complaint, and perhaps, in regard to the lice she had been justified. 'From a certain point of view,' she could complain, about Bolinka first of all, who had suddenly been forgotten, even though the path of the lice had begun with her, and furthermore, she could complain of the crucifixion of being uprooted and nailed here for months on foreign soil, crawling with every kind of misery. . . . But a complaint, even justified, was no more than a flickering candle, and already the bright sky shone overhead, with dark shadows streaking by, the death trout, announcing the great day of damnation. Besides, whom could she blame? She shook her head in despair.

'May I go now?' she asked humbly.

'May she go now?' repeated the interpreter, turning towards the old German. 'She says she would have to take her clothes off to find them. That would be dangerous. They would get everywhere.'

'She'll go when I tell her to go!' the director yelled furiously. 'What are all these objections, demands, complaints, anyway? I want discipline and respect here, lice or no lice! I've told you before. . . .

'There's no need for her to undress here. Let her go back to her dormitory, find a little box and catch some of her lice. One louse or ten, I don't care. I just want proof, proof I tell you! Don't you ever understand, for Christ's sake! Come back here in fifteen minutes with your box. Hurry up!'

The bewildered woman had understood this last part of the instructions and was waiting to hear the rest. But as the German waved his arm, the interpreter pushed her out saying,

'Put some in a box and come back here!' The woman fled across the camp, where someone was picking at a mandolin, where, behind the little windows of a barracks building, a woman was combing her hair before a broken mirror, another one was ladling soup into a tin can, where blackout curtains were being drawn, and overhead, the sky of Pomerania, left to itself, sent the silence, the clouds, the nomadic hordes rushing on their way, before the dangers of the night.

When she arrived in the dormitory, the woman with the lice laid the soup which had been served in her absence, on the stove.

'Thanks for saving this. But watch it a bit longer, would you please?' she asked her neighbour. 'I've just caught lice, and I have to put some in a box.'

The other woman stared at her and slipped out of the little alley between the two beds.

'You know what? Maria's gone crazy!' she shouted to the others who sat perched on their high bedsteads or around the stove, or at a table decorated with paper festoons, talking about food, the winter, sometimes men, all the things that lay at the edge of their deprived world, the winter biting closer than the rest, into their hands especially, like a pet dog.

'I'm telling you, Maria's gone crazy!' she repeated in a loud voice, glancing cautiously between the two beds. 'She's talking about putting lice in a box!'

But Maria, bare to the waist, holding her shirt in her hands, came out of the shadows to defend herself.

'Let me explain!' she cried in her rather hoarse voice which her fellow prisoners often ridiculed. 'Let me explain!'

The women had now descended upon her.

'Watch out for the soup on the stove!' she cried at them.

A waste of breath. Questions rained down upon her.

'So you really have lice? Are you sure? Why do you want to put them in a box? To punish them, is that it? Or are they a present for your boyfriend? No, she probably wants to train them!'

Bewildered by this barrage of remarks, the woman with the yellow hair stepped back between the beds, and, with a sudden impulse of modesty, held her shirt against her chest. The others came after her.

'Oh come on, no one wants to take them away from you! . . .'

Finally she succeeded in making herself heard. She said that the camp director wanted proof and she had to obey him, after all. Then she asked for a box. Someone gave her an empty match box. It was peaceful again but they all still hung around her.

'I need more light,' declared Maria, coming out from between the beds.

The others leapt back in a hurry.

All of a sudden she felt very powerful.

'Don't worry,' she said. 'They hold on tight and they don't jump. . . .'

Soon she was naked beneath the lamp. She was inspecting the seams of her coarse grey underwear. In the early stages, the lice do not venture beyond this innermost layer. They are so close, then, that apart from the biting, they blend in easily with the body's inner life; they become no more than a rather abstract sign of mortification, and while inducing melancholy, the only larvae they produce are those of weariness.

Later on, they will become tireless prospectors of that little-known human geology, which superimposes, around an inner fire and a matrix of white clay, layers of tufa, of felt and velvet humus, studded with corollas of agate, all within that luke-warm human darkness, in which one can hear the scratchy rustle of cloth at every movement, like a dry ocean.

When the heat of summer become too oppressive, or when competition in the depths becomes too strong, they will finally venture into the light of day, on your sleeve perhaps, stranded in a landscape of the tertiary period, blind, translucent, with their shrimplike legs, and there, let themselves be caught, curling up remorsefully like woodlice.

They were all looking at the woman who stood naked beneath the lamp. They helped her count. The lice which she was gathering were asleep, clinging obstinately to the folds of her underwear. Still underfed, many were pale and ghostly; a louse without its drop of blood looks like the X-ray of a louse.

'Six!'

That was proof enough. After closing the matchbox, Maria gathered up her clothes and went back between the beds to get dressed. She kept the box clutched in her hand. Meanwhile, everyone was still watching her and fame was going to her head.

'What do you think of that?' she asked the other women insolently, as she waved the matchbox above her head. 'Now I've got a weapon!'

Most of the women understood her to mean simply the newly sharpened but soon blunted weapon which she would use to convince the camp director. But for others her words

8*

evoked other, more sinister images. Her weapon was like a handful of seeds. One can always fend off a blow, no matter how sudden. But if someone throws a heavy, suspicious-looking coat in your face, a filthy rag, a crawling head of hair, a whole swarming prairie! . . .

'I'm off now,' said the woman who had finished putting her lice-infested clothes back on, still clutching her matchbox.

She walked to the door and went out. Her neighbour, Nadia, slipped out behind her. In the darkness of the courtyard she clutched Maria's arm.

'What do you want?' asked the woman with the lice. 'Let go! Let me go or I'll give them to you!'

'Yes, give me some!' whispered the other. 'You have six in your box. Four will do just as well, and with the two others, tomorrow or the day after, I could ask for two days off. All you have to do is put two of them in here. Maria, as a favour!'

She whipped a little tin out of her pocket.

'I'll make holes in the cover so they can breathe. Please, Maria, just for me. I kept an eye on your soup.'

'Are you keeping an eye on it now?' asked the woman harshly.

'I'll go back as soon as you give them to me. . . . You certainly are mean!' cried Nadia in a crushed voice as the other started on her way. 'Besides, are they really yours? Do they belong to you? I'll bet you got them from somebody else!'

Now she was barring the path of the woman with the lice.

'I'm only asking you for them because it's easier that way. But don't worry, they'll get to me by themselves. When you're asleep tonight, I can very easily slip my shirt into your bed, without your noticing. Or I could do it like this. . . .'

She suddenly wrapped her arms around Maria and pressed against her, laughing and saying,

'I would rather not have had them on me, but since you're so stupid and mean!'

Frightened, the woman with the lice tried to break loose from her embrace, but the box in her hand made it difficult.

' . . . now they are getting on me and you can't do anything about it!' Nadia went on, panting in her companion's face. 'Wait! Don't go yet! Give them a little longer!'

But the other woman had already succeeded in breaking away. She moved back a few steps, brushing her yellow hair out of her eyes.

'Are you going mad, Nadia?' she cried, breathless.

Then as the determined woman started to bear down upon her again,

'Stop!' she said. 'I'll give you some, just to have a little peace. Come over here with your box.'

The two women moved over towards a wall. It was lit by the moon; there would be planes that night. The women with the lice opened the matchbox cautiously, and shook it gently over the tin which her companion held open against her chest. The species had another nasty trait; they were invisible in the moonlight.

'Two must have fallen out,' muttered Maria. 'Put the cover on. Hurry up!'

She herself snapped the matchbox shut so hard that it jumped out of her hand and fell to the ground. Her companion leaned over quickly to pick it up and handed it back to her after slipping her own little tin in her pocket to keep her hands free: a busy, confused little exchange. In the sky, the moon passed from behind some clouds and cast furtive shadows, as though of thieves, against the wall. The two women soon separated.

'I'll keep an eye on your soup, Maria!' cried Nadia.

A few seconds later, Maria knocked at the camp director's door. His brow knit in anxiety, he was listening to reports on the radio about Allied bombers over Germany. The interpreter was still nearby, with an equally anxious expression on her face.

'Let me see!' she said dryly to the woman who was holding out her matchbox. Pinching her lips, she took it, pushed the little drawer open squeamishly, and snapped it shut.

'She's right,' the interpreter said to the old German. 'It is
definitely a louse. . . .'

She threw the matchbox to Maria who caught it in midair.

'A louse. . . . Well, then, one day off, just one,' muttered the
director, still listening to the information being delivered by
the monotone voice of a military announcer.

Suddenly his attention was riveted to the broadcast.

'Now they're coming our way,' he declared. 'Tell everyone
to put out the lights, Mariouchka, and you, get going!' he
added to the woman with the lice.

Then he sat back in his armchair, wearily. The night would
be another holocaust.

This holocaust (the alert lasted for a long time but there was
no destruction at Schweinemünde) was followed by another,
set off by the lice, seemingly negligible, in the dark dormitory
where the women slept. It consisted less of the discreet, rather
sporadic fire which smouldered on Maria's body, as it did of the
calculations to which the lice gave rise.

Once back in the barracks, her tin tightly closed and hidden
in her pocket, Nadia had not been able to resist telling the
others about the strategy which she had just devised. Everyone
had praised her with the over-exuberant language, the cheap
superlatives with which they tried – rather feebly, it must be
admitted – to enhance the poverty of their existence. Already
they could anticipate a vast exchange of vermin, a friendly
pooling of resources, so organized that each of the women, in
turn, could enjoy a day or two of rest.

But, reduced to this one benefit, the rewards of the strategy,
pleasant as they were, would have seemed rather limited, if, at
the same time, the lice had not acquired a subversive value and,
deadly as termites, threatened the very foundations of the
camp. Once infested with lice as a group, or in any case bearing
the indelible stigma of vermin, the women would become, they
thought, difficult to employ in the factory, where their duties
brought them in contact with the German workers.

Moreover, their ranks would be depleted by absenteeism and very soon the entire camp would become suspect. It was high time. Misery, in the end, was bound to fester in the open, like the obscene revenge of corpses, and the reign of lice was bound to assert itself, stealthily, insidiously, like a reign of remorse. Yes, it was high time that the others began to find 'that certain thing' crushed under their fingernails.

Such were the dreams of some of the women, Nadia among them, while in the distance, the night, furrowed with bombers, was unloading upon the earth its hitherto unsuspected burden of thunder. In her bed, Nadia was scratching. 'I've been thinking too much about lice,' she said to herself. She couldn't possibly have picked them up from her brief contact with Maria. Of course the transfer, from box to box, had taken place rather haphazardly, groping in the darkness.

She slipped her hand beneath the folded overcoat which served as a pillow. The box containing the lice was there, safe and sound. As she lay down again, her hand returned to her burning groin, to the persistent frenzy of a sort of sterile, blind masturbation.

Nadia waited for two days before presenting her lice to the camp director. She thought this delay was necessary in order not to enrage him or send him into a panic. The rhythm of contagion had to be skilfully paced. Nadia's shrewdness, however, could have been her undoing. The two lice died in the box. But others, from where she did not know, perhaps simply born of desire, now inhabited her body. Very much alive, these. As she gathered them, she could feel them struggle between the cushions of her pinched fingertips.

With the proof under his nose, the camp director simply nodded his head and agreed to the requested exemption. He had very quickly 'taken stock of the problem' – as he put it. The only station which had the equipment for effective fumigation, the only steamroom in the region, lay about fifty kilometres from Schweinemünde. There was not enough gasoline for the trucks which could carry the women to this headquarters, and now there was even beginning to be a shortage of coal to heat the steam rooms. So the delousing would have to take place right here, from day to day – one more temporary expedient. And there was no point in raising one's eyes to heaven; the threat of the evening planes, night and day, intercepted the gaze of the great Witness.

'Ask them to sign here,' the old German said wearily to the interpreter, handing her a few sheets of paper. 'That will at least give us some statistics to cover ourselves, if we should need proof someday.'

That particular evening, two women had come to the office (inseparable friends as the interpreter was well aware), according to the new custom, each with her little box of lice. Nadia had exchanged hers for a few pieces of bread. Now that the lice were in such demand, those who had them to spare had no trouble distributing them. If Nadia hadn't organized an orderly system, the others might have stampeded the camp director, all together, or at least in cliques or couples. This way, they drew lots to see whose turn it was, two by two to make the day of leisure more pleasant.

This procedure was too reasonable for anyone to think of objecting. Just the same, it caused a good deal of heartache among the women. Sealed up in boxes, the lice died after two or three days. The market crashed. Women begged those who were not yet endowed to buy their lice at rock-bottom prices. 'Then you'll be able to draw lots tomorrow night. I'm sure you'll win. I know I haven't a chance. And just think, maybe the factory will be bombed the day after. No, for me it's not the same thing; I haven't much to look forward to in life. . . .' All of a sudden, the market had become desperately sluggish. Then some of the more desperate women let the vermin loose upon their bodies. They were thus able to preserve their wealth, to see it bear fruit.

From then on life was smooth. A golden age had come, in which lice rained like coins into every hand, multiplying into such vast denominations, that everyone was soon bathed in opulent equality, paid for only by insomnia and self-disgust. Every evening, lots were drawn to see who would get off work in the factory next day. The camp director seemed resigned to this routine of exemptions. He required only that a record be kept of the names, so that he could watch for those who came back several times and thus ferret out the real 'incendiaries' in his inflamed flock.

But once armed with proof of a certain number of relapses, he suddenly found himself helpless. The women, infested with lice to varying degrees, came in close contact with one another all day long; to catch lice a second or a third time could just as well be the result of a kind of innocence, revealing that among the prisoners, there existed certain perpetual victims, certain unwitting intermediaries, whom it would have been futile to punsih.

It took him some time to convince himself that there was no longer a 'source' – if, indeed, there ever had been – that lice as an element could appear to withdraw temporarily and yet remain intact, in short, that they were a kind of ocean brought into being once and for all, with deceptive tides, waves, an ebb and flow, and that therefore none of the women would be free from lice for very long at a time, and finally, that he and the interpreter had now caught them too.

'I don't want a single one of those boxes brought in here any more!' he declared to the interpreter. 'Proof is no longer necessary. I have notified the management of the factory that every day, for a month, three women will automatically remain in camp to get rid of their vermin.'

He had tried to persuade the authorities that it would be wise to build a new dormitory in the camp, to house the women who were freshly deloused, but that would also have implied preventing all contact between the clean women and those who were still infested, and work at the factory did not permit such segregation.

The Ukrainian women had already been withdrawn from the

workshops, where they stood next to the German men, without any great loss, as it turned out, for there was now a shortage of electricity and production had been cut back. They were set to work pushing wheelbarrows in the courtyard or shovelling coal. To wake them from their daydreams, the German supervisor threw large stones at them, from a distance. But it was a losing battle.

The machinery of lice, of contagion, of drawing lots and bargaining, began to creak, here and there. The women whose names were never drawn were already threatening to revolt. Never deloused, smarting with bites, they acted merely as carriers, which infuriated them because they never profited from their misery. Those whose names were drawn too often (victims or not) were eventually suspected of negligence by the camp director. He harassed them during their day off. When they saw him passing under their windows, they ran to their beds to wrap themselves in a blanket. He entered the dormitory and walked up to the stove where the clothes were boiling.

'The blankets too!' he ordered coolly, without looking at the women.

They had to obey. Slowly, resentfully, the lice-infested women removed the covers which they had wrapped around themselves. The camp director continued to watch the big kettles, but, alerted no doubt by the swishing of the woollen covers, or by the martyred sighs of the women, he knew that his orders had been carried out. Then he strolled back towards the door. It was only just as he was about to open it that he whipped about.

'What a pack of witches!' he yelled, laughing.

Naked, circling about the steaming cauldrons, their stringy hair still damp from the showers and hanging over their shoulders, the women seemed to be concocting a fiendish brew; only the moonlit clearing was missing, the flat stones of the Brocken, but, in these sinister times, the magic of daylight made up generously for this lack of legendary landmarks.

The old German had already gone out the door, slamming it

after him, with a muffled laugh. Behind his racial contempt lay the attitude of an impertinent schoolboy, hiding his impotence behind a long, idiotic snicker, as he beats a cowardly retreat.

He, usually so aloof, who could very well have used his prestige, his authority, to look at the naked women, to paw them, to force them into degrading positions, instead demeaned himself, stealing away after a moment of mocking laughter, a taunt that stung, but was immediately reduced to a hideous grating sound, like the creak of charcoal. It was rape, of a kind. The man penetrates you slowly, unbearably, like a wry grin. The grin was there, suddenly planted within you, but the man was gone. Better not to even think about it.

The dead lice swirled about the boiling kettles as though in a merry-go-round. In the end, they disappeared like magic. When alive, beneath one's fingernails, they had been tight and hard, their translucent skin stretched taut over a feverish, stubborn droplet of life. In the hot water, they had to burst, evaporate, dissolve, return to the faraway refuge where the sting of the nettle, the bitter hips of the wild rose, and remorse of all kinds are kept ignited.

And so, on all sides, the craze for lice began to lose hold. Everyone came back to earth. No one had been saved from death by the strategy, for the factory had not been bombed once since the appearance of the vermin. The only thing which had been gained was a few days of leisure and open skies. Even this pleasure cancelled itself out, in a silence more tragic than pain.

But it was too late to turn back. The lice were now a part of existence, as universal as salt. The kettles of boiling water, which steamed in the dormitory from morning to night, would never quench the voracious thirst which the lice kept alive on each female body. These kettles were like the effervescent springs found in places of pilgrimage, visited by revelation, inhabited by the Holy Spirit; or the wells in which fiancées and sterile women throw pins, coins, and rings.

Here the women immersed their clothes out of a desire for purification, no doubt, but also for the joy of eradicating something which had become both a welcome and a shameful part of their existence. For, whether hatred or desire, or both at once, the lice had never ceased being a form of 'revenge', revenge against enforced privation, against authority, against the relentless absence of men.

In lice was a fanatic desire to be banished, a desire to complete the nauseous semi-exile which kept you apart from life and from men, to scoff at one's passion, and, deprived of love, to enjoy the pleasure of destroying a living creature, born of oneself.

That was the situation when, one morning, the Allied planes dropped on part of the factory and the town what was called in those days a 'carpet of bombs', but which, in fact, was more like a fiery harrow. Working slightly apart from the central buildings, the women had time to take shelter and paid but a meagre tribute to the powers of the sky; only one of them was killed and three others lightly wounded.

Smoke rose above the debris, quickly dispersed by the wind, while an odour of chalk and fresh cement lingered on, rising from the upheaved earth, the emanation of a quarry under which men were crying out like rabbits. Because a large part of the factory remained standing, damaged only slightly, work continued the next day. The women were set to work clearing the rubble but it soon became clear that they were not equal to the job. The German authorities asked for reinforcements. And so about a hundred Russian men, deported into Germany at the beginning of the war, came to be interned at Schweinemünde.

Barracks had been built for them, opposite the women's camp, on the other side of the road which led through this no man's land to the town dump. The new constructions, like those which housed the women, were surrounded with barbed wire. Any conversation which passed through this double sieve retained only its essence, its priceless message. Our mental world was to owe much to these stakes, with their blue, vibrating hedge of spines.

The men arrived one night and, as soon as the first glow of morning appeared, the women looked over at them in the shadows. Most of the men were very tall and stood facing them (for who knows how long), as though daybreak lay in that direction.

They yelled out friendly greetings in Ukrainian to the first women who came out of the barracks, but soon the whistle blew, the signal to gather outside the dormitory, and there were suddenly such swarming numbers of women that the men, overwhelmed by the miracle, could only lean against their side of the barbed wire, speechless, smiling in a kind of dismay.

The slow, everyday routine took over again very quickly. The men were put to work in the bombed-out section of town. They were gone until evening, when they sat out in front of their barracks, playing harmonicas, singing and shouting compliments to the women. They called out, asking them to sing too, and clapped their hands now and then to make the women dance.

The camp director came out of his office. Was he dealing with savages? To dance with lice on one's body revealed a staggering lack of self-respect. it was like savouring one's filth, or deliberately using the steps of the dance to show off the barbaric tattoos left by the vermin. For a moment, he thought of forbidding all such amusements, but he caught himself in time. He had finally realized that to frustrate the women was futile; they simply 'swallowed their resentment', although, to be exact, it was more a matter of swallowing vermin.

'Here is what I am going to do!' he declared triumphantly to the interpreter as he came back to his office that evening. 'I will give permission for the men to come dance in our camp on Sundays, as soon as all the lice are gone. You can post a notice to that effect. And make sure they understand. I'll discuss it with my colleague, Ernst, over there. . . .'

The interpreter, who had picked up a sheet of paper to translate the announcement into her own language, started at the director's last few words.

'If you say anything over there, you will spoil everything,' she said without looking at him, twirling her fountain pen between her fingers. 'The women will be humiliated and they'll never get over it. Even when they have no more lice, the men will think that they still do, that they once had them and that they could easily come back again. You will destroy something between them!' she cried in a brazen voice that was quite unlike herself and made her blush to the very roots of her black hair, pulled back beneath a white kerchief.

The old German burst out laughing and pointed his thick forefinger at her,

'Do you want to know what I think? You're speaking for yourself right now, Mariouchka. Yes, for yourself,' he repeated, leaning over closer to her.

'I'm not. I have no interest in them,' answered the interpreter. 'I am speaking for the women in the camp. If you want to play on the women's feelings to bring a little order back here, I don't think you should try to humiliate them. You are playing into the hands of the lice.'

'So I'm playing into the hands of the lice, am I?' roared the old German as though he had been slapped in the face, staggering out of his chair.

'What I meant is that you might give the camp a bad reputation. . . .' stammered the interpreter, feeling herself sink deeper at every word.

'A bad reputation!' the director repeated, muttering between his teeth. 'But they didn't start on me, for God's sake! They didn't start on German soil!' he shouted, pointing at the small window, beyond which lay the land of Pomerania, drowned in evening mists. 'They come from you, from you and your race, you and your dirty minds!

'Or maybe from you, yourself! Yes, you! You're better educated, more intelligent than the others. But appearances can deceive! Maybe you're betraying me. Who knows! Maybe you are slyly undermining my authority!

'I see you coming every evening, every damn evening, with another lousy woman. You always act like a big sister, the woman sits there looking at her feet while you put words in her mouth. Every evening, when this lice business comes up, you are right here. You know everything before the woman even opens her mouth and you decide, you often make decisions without even bothering to consult me. You don't even realize any more how presumptuous you're getting!

'. . . "Watch out! A new crop of lice has been found in Room 4. Watch out! These women should not go to work tomorrow. Watch out, you will humiliate them!" Lice, lice, lice. You and your lice! All of you and your lice! What about me, the Director, where do I fit in?'

The old German had shrieked these last words. He was standing, clutching his desk with both hands. His lower lip trembled. The interpreter rose and left the room, her shoulders bent under the onslaught. Two women, attracted by the loud voices, and noticing an opportunity to sympathize with the one who usually gave them orders, began to question her softly, as soon as she had shut the door.

'Ever since the lice came, its been the same every evening,' the interpreter murmured, unable to hold back her tears. 'Every evening, he finds another excuse to keep after me.'

Then she fled quickly towards the back of the camp. Harmonicas could still be heard and, on both sides of the barbed wire, the men and women, already lost in the evening mist and unable to see one another, continued their patient parading.

The camp director talked to his colleague Ernst about this method of blackmail which he had just thought up.

'It's my last attempt,' he said. 'If it doesn't work, there's nothing left to do but set fire to this whole confounded nest of vermin!'

He gestured threateningly at the barracks of his camp. The other man looked at him severely. Another one who was letting himself go, who was 'losing his nerve' as the newspapers said, denouncing those whose discouragement in this fourth year of the war was – or so they said – a form of desertion.

'An interesting idea,' Ernst replied coldly. 'But I intend to use it differently. The men will be permitted to visit the women's camp on Sunday if the week's production shows an increase. I keep weekly figures, so many cubic metres. . . . Wait! Let me finish!' he added, raising his hand to silence his colleague, who was already preparing to argue that this did not suit his plans at all. 'Of course, if at the end of the week, your women still have lice, the reward will be postponed. I'll find an excuse of some kind. . . .'

'That's simple enough. Just tell them the truth!' cried the women's camp director. 'That will mortify my women and spur them on.'

Ernst shook his head.

'No,' he said dryly. 'My dear fellow, of course one must use authority, a strong grip, to handle prisoners, but sometimes it is also necessary to use a bit of psy-chol-o-gy.' He enumerated each syllable as though teaching a new word to someone less informed than himself. 'I want my men to go on being attracted to your women; I want to keep them aroused. The end result will be so many more cubic metres. Do you understand?'

The other man understood; he understood that the benefit of his scheme would go directly to his colleague, that production was the only thing that counted in the eyes of their superiors, that Ernst, when all was said and done, would receive the congratulations and the promotions. He suddenly began to hate this clever man who stood in front of him: he alone would score, thanks to the lice, and the women would not have to suffer humiliation. He himself would be the only one to pay for the appearance of the vermin. Even the interpreter would triumph, in a certain sense, for Ernst was echoing the same arguments which she had advanced the evening before, and had won his point. Once again he thought of setting fire to this nest of vermin, but this time he kept the idea to himself.

He returned to the women's camp and ordered the interpreter to post the notice. He spoke to her roughly; he would have liked to hit her but Mariouchka (he had given her this nickname himself, in the early days, when he had found her gentleness and youth touching) hastened to carry out his orders. She left very quickly, though not without a sigh.

'No sighing, I tell you! No sighing!' shrieked the director, so loud that his throat rasped.

He leapt after her but banged into the door which she had closed behind her.

'No sighing!' he screamed once again, for his own benefit, as he came back to his desk.

He was an unhappy man.

As she fled towards the women's dormitories, the interpreter heard the director's cries. How he had changed, in the last three weeks! Before the lice had come, he had always kept a little sheltered spot for her, in his severity towards the women, where now and then, for no apparent reason, she would feel a furtive ray of warmth, as though, through a break in the clouds of war, she had glimpsed the sunshine of friendship, a great summer of fraternity. She had felt protected then, all the more protected in that the paw that was laid upon her was heavy, with sharp, though retracted claws. . . . She was the chosen one. Now that the sun was again behind the clouds and the dry litanies of her job continued, she remembered this warm ray, inconstant because of the war, but not extinguished.

Because of the lice, she found herself in the biting cold of winter, beneath a sky overcast with threats. Would they ever get rid of this vermin? Would they ever get rid of Evil? 'The easiest way,' she thought, 'would be to burn down the barracks. . . .' For it was foolish to think that this notice could do any good.

She read it to the others, who listened in silence.

'But I don't have any, right now!' declared one of the women when the interpreter had finished reading. 'That's not fair! Why should I wait for everybody else to get rid of theirs? They should put me somewhere by myself. Otherwise I'll catch them again! . . .'

'What about the old ones?' cried another woman. 'What do they care about men and dancing? They won't bother to get rid of their lice. They'll keep them forever!'

The 'old ones' (four or five women who were approaching fifty) protested: at any rate they were cleaner than the younger women who spent all their time combing their hair instead of washing their clothes. Soon all the women were talking at once in loud voices. Some found reasons to be hopeful: one or two nights of communal clothes washing would take care of the vermin; others despaired: the lice had settled permanently in the straw mattresses, between the bed boards, and in the cracks of the floor; still others began to compare the alternatives; they questioned men's love, its gentleness, its sincerity. The others soon silenced them.

It was decided that they would all sacrifice one night of sleep; that they would light fires (the wood from the bombed-out buildings furnished plenty of fuel) and scrub everything, right down to the floor of the dormitory.

'But how are we going to prove to him that we have got rid of them?' one of the women asked all of a sudden, after a while, when everything was quiet again.

The one who had spoken had gone out into the courtyard with the others to wait for the evening roll call. Night had fallen. The motionless silhouettes of a few of the men could be made out, placed there as though on sentry duty, which always arouses, unintentionally, a natural state of anticipation, of nostalgia and sadness, and which morning can break only with difficulty.

How tall they loomed! Just at the moment when the women were doing all they could to make them less distant, they discovered, with a certain alarm, how rigid, how substantial the

men's bodies were, how silent in the night, and they felt this
weight upon them, like statues.

'Yes, how can we prove that we have got rid of them?'
repeated the woman.

She was right, of course. There was no problem in proving
the opposite; proof crawled all over you. But purity, if they
ever achieved it again, had no obvious symptoms. One was
simply deprived of proof, forced to appeal to the judge's good
faith.

'We will give him our word of honour that they are gone,'
replied another woman.

'Then why don't we do it right away?' asked another. 'Or
if you think it might be more convincing, we could wait a
few days – just as long as we do it.'

'What about them?' someone objected, pointing to the men
lingering watchfully on the other side of the barbed wire.
'They'll catch them. Then they'll complain and we'll be dis-
honoured.'

They were ready to entertain all kinds of shady calculations.
If they did not succeed in getting rid of the lice, why not lie and
at least see the men once? After all, they might be dead
tomorrow.

In spite of this temptation, the women worked all night
boiling their clothes, washing their bodies, and cleaning every
last nook and cranny of the dormitory. Since the clothes had
to be dry by morning, the two stoves had been stoked until
they were red hot. It was hard to breathe in this Turkish bath
atmosphere, the women were slipping on the wet floor, stumbling over the pails, swearing at one another across the laundry
lines.

One woman, who was wringing out clothes over a tub and
who had been talking for a long time in the same thoughtful,
droning voice, said to her neighbour.

'. . . no, with men it's a bit more complicated. It's all in how
they look at things, certain things. I don't know if you understand what I'm trying to say. It's not that I think they're so

very selfish, the way you do, it's that . . . but no, it's hard to explain. . . .'

Just then a pail sitting on the stove boiled over. Everyone began to yell again. Far away, in the night, an air raid warning sounded.

Before three days were up, Nadia, the one who came from Lepodiska, near Kiev, and whose idea it had been to exchange lice in the first place, had to surrender to the evidence: the lice had survived the night of the great cleaning. There was no hope.

Nadia, more than any of the others, had made the extermination of the lice her 'personal affair'. For while the rest of them looked through the double hedge of barbed wire and saw a collective masculine presence, for which a place had been reserved within them since the beginning of time, and resumed that endless dialogue which silence cannot interrupt, Nadia had recognized *a* man, one of those beings – perhaps the only one – who have been waiting for a long time in the wings of your life, leaning back patiently until the sunshine of the present should stream down upon them.

In the evening, she tried to keep apart from the women who were pressing against the barbed wire, like a fenced-in herd tortured by thirst on a summer day. Her own thirst was of a different sort, and now and then tightened her throat as though she were unable to swallow.

Walking up and down the long bare spaces, quite far off from the motionless pack of her fellow inmates, Nadia deliberately banished herself from her species, creating around herself a wider and wider zone of that grey emptiness which surrounds lost animals, as they run about aimlessly, looking at the sky with wild eyes, grazing upon thistles in their distraction, while in the distance, the watering hour and the clinking of chains can be heard.

A few days earlier he had shouted his name to her: Piotr, pointing at his chest. He was very blond and wore a dirty white fatigue cap like a soldier. She had answered him the same way, blushing, for she was pointing to her bosom of which she was very proud. Now she felt a lump in her throat.

From time to time she would spot him in the distance, he, too, somewhat apart from the others. He looked at her and waved. No, she did not want him to know that she had had lice, that she could have them again tomorrow, that she had them now, in fact, for between the crawling past and the crawling future there was hardly time for a hand to reach out and be drawn back. One could not take advantage of such a brief respite.

Sometimes a delegation of the women would come to talk to Nadia.

'Listen, Nadia, we've tried everything and you have to admit there is nothing else to do. But if we all agree, we can go to the director and tell him that we are all rid of them, that they are destroyed. That way the men will come on Sunday and we can have some fun. Then we'll see what happens. It's better than nothing.'

'No. We have no right to do that,' replied Nadia. 'I'll tell the director that you are lying; I'll prove it to him. . . .'

'Why don't we have the right?' the women cried.

'The men didn't ask to catch them.'

'Ha! If they come here, they're asking for it,' said the woman who believed that men were selfish. 'Besides, if you give us away, we'll tell him that you were the one who started keeping them in a box!'

'We've all had our little boxes, at one time or another,' Nadia replied calmly.

They parted with insults. Since Nadia had stopped looking at him while she had been talking to the women, the man with the white cap had gone back into the barracks. No, this torture could not go on. . . .

Nadia could not sleep. The thought that she was responsible for spreading the lice nagged at her. But how could she have foreseen that as soon as you touch them, as soon as you breathe your intentions, they are all over you, like a broken necklace?

And it wasn't only on your body! Nakedness is smooth, offering very few refuges to these wind-blown particles, clothes are a risky shelter, easily explored, but not the furniture, the beds, the floors, the walls!

'Someone should set fire to this dormitory,' thought Nadia, tossing and turning in her bed. 'And it should go up very quickly so there would be no time to save anything.'

At that moment, in the camp director's office, Mariouchka, at the limit of her endurance, was bursting into tears. The old German had been torturing her for more than an hour with absurd questions, accusations, threats.

'Do you hear me! I refuse to believe anything any more! I won't believe a word!' he yelled. 'Don't come around to-morrow or the next day telling me that they have got rid of them. I'll kill you on the spot!'

He had suddenly realized that there was no possible proof that all the lice were exterminated, and felt as if he were going out of his mind.

'But they still have them,' Mariouchka replied feebly. 'They washed everything and they still have them. . . .'

'You needn't act so pathetic about it!' said the old German between his teeth. 'Because you've got what you wanted, didn't you? You won! They still have them! You love being able to say that, to rub it in, don't you! They still have them!'

'But really,' whimpered Mariouchka, 'what do you want me to say?'

'You're asking me?' screamed the camp director. 'I'm sup-posed to know what they've done with their lice? Are you trying to make fun of me? . . . No, don't go away! We're not through yet!'

The interpreter sat down and hid her face in her hands.

'He got fifty extra cubic metres, over there,' continued the director, wringing his thick, veined hands. 'What about us? Where do we stand, I'm asking you? Do you hear me?'

'Yes,' answered Mariouchka in a voice flooded with tears.

Then, utterly worn out, she added:

'Now what?'

'Now . . . ' the old German echoed, his anger suddenly deflated. 'Now . . .'

He did not finish the sentence.

The interpreter, surprised by his silence, raised her head. They looked at one another without hatred, just as when, at the end of a long ordeal of violence, one reaches the bare, stone plateau where mass murders and ritual crimes are enacted in silence.

It was not until the middle of the following night that a cry rang out of nowhere and tore all the women from sleep; flames were issuing from a corner of the dormitory. Smoke already filled the room but the fire itself could not be seen right away, for it had started beneath the building, among the pilings which raised it slightly from the ground. Hardly had the women leapt from their beds when loud crackling noises were heard and the smoke grew thicker. There was instant panic. Shrieking, clutching an armful of clothes, the women stampeded towards the door.

Once outside, the glow from the fire dazzled them. At times, the wind levelled the flames and then, when it subsided, they rose higher, waking nestfuls of sparks on the wooden beams, twisting into sputtering cornucopias. The dormitory was now a solid, blazing mass, so intense, so dazzling that the women who clustered several metres away with their piles of clothing at their feet had to hold their hands before their eyes and look away, as though in the face of great tribulation.

But actually, though they might have mourned for a moment over the loss of a treasured possession, their last link to certain memories, they discovered, in the face of this destruction, the extent of their poverty, the meagreness of what lay in the ashes. They felt unburdened.

The camp director was running about in all directions,

swearing. His colleague, Ernst, had joined him after ordering his men out of their barracks, thinking at first that they might help fight the fire. But it spread too rapidly to leave room for hope.

'There's nothing you can do now, old fellow,' he shouted to the director. 'Relax, there's nothing left to save.'

The heat was becoming unbearable. The women had retreated against the barbed wire enclosure and, asphyxiated by the smoke which the wind blew back upon them, terrified by the clouds of sparks, they began to shriek again. Ernst, who had taken over command, decided to let them come into the men's camp.

They followed obediently, their reddened eyes suddenly opening wide, after the glare of the fire, upon this miracle of darkness and dancing shadows. A dormitory was prepared for them in an unoccupied section of the men's barracks. But they did not feel like retiring into it much before morning. Until then, the crackling glow of the fire kept them out in the open. The fire glowed for a long time. They talked quietly in the bright silence of the night, with voices that grew more and more subdued. Soon it became difficult to distinguish the men from the women. Slightly apart from the others, Nadia and the man in the white cap stood facing each other, exchanging trivialities with the oblique glances of those who burn with the desire to press their mouths together. . . .

The investigation attributed the fire to an incendiary bomb dropped by the planes which had flown over the camp that night.

Two days later, through a door in the dormitory which had been left open, the women saw a man, naked to the waist, who seemed to be looking for lice in his clothes.

'Oh, it's nothing,' one of the other men replied when questioned. 'We all have them, now and again, some worse than others. But we're getting used to it after two years. . . .'

And from then on, no one ever spoke of them. After all, as

far as the lice went, perhaps it had only been a matter of that which is running about everywhere, spreading, swarming, insinuating itself, burning, shimmering in transparency, kindling hostility, igniting loneliness, joining like to like, hiding, seeking itself, that carrier of contagion sometimes known as the soul. . . .

translated by Merloyd Lawrence